THE BUTTERFLIES OF SUFFOLK
AN ATLAS & HISTORY

Howard
Mendel

Steven H
Piotrowski

Published by

SUFFOLK NATURALISTS' SOCIETY

1986

Published by The Suffolk Naturalists' Society, c/o The Museum, High Street, Ipswich IP1 3QH.

First published 1986

ISBN 0-9508154-1-1

Sponsored by Associated Tyre Specialists (A.T.S.) Ltd. and the World Wildlife Fund, U.K.

WWF

Typesetting: Monarch Origination, Hadleigh Road, Ipswich.

Printed by: Ancient House Press, Hadleigh Road Industrial Estate, Ipswich.

CONTENTS

FOREWORD

by Sam Beaufoy, M.B.E., F.R.P.S.

FOR OVER FIFTY YEARS, life-history studies, and photography of Suffolk's butterfly species from life, have absorbed my leisure hours. As a member of the Suffolk Naturalists' Society since 1944, I knew well its founder Claude Morley, editor of the *"Lepidoptera of Suffolk"* (1937a), and the late H.E. Chipperfield, whose meticulous annual review of the County's Lepidoptera appeared in the Society's Transactions until 1984. Since I began to take an interest in butterflies I have seen great changes in the numbers of these beautiful insects in Suffolk. In the 1940's and 1950's I could always be sure of seeing the Purple Emperor, White Admiral, Pearl-bordered, High Brown and Silver-washed Fritillaries, Large Tortoiseshell, Grizzled and Dingy Skippers around the Belstead and Raydon Woods, in south-east Suffolk. Wonderful years indeed. However, 1960 marked the beginning of the decline in numbers of these species, and in particular the Purple Emperor and Large Tortoiseshell. The number of White Admirals diminished yearly.

Several reasons for this decline have been put forward. Certainly some woodlands, including Belstead and Raydon, were subjected to drastic felling; the replacement of indigenous trees by conifers completely changed the habitat. Hedges have been removed, denying butterflies a "pathway" from one suitable area to another. Field edges and roadside verges have been sprayed with pesticides and herbicides. In addition, 1960-62 was a period when there was a significant fall in both summer and overall average temperatures. Possibly the unusual coldness affected all species, but whereas the commoner ones were eventually able to build up their numbers again, the rarer ones could not. It should never be assumed however that a butterfly is "extinct" in an area because it has not been seen there for several consecutive years. It may be surviving at a low level, but unobserved, in some remaining pocket of suitable habitat.

The Butterfly Survey has been of immense value. It brings our knowledge up-to-date, and traces the fate of Suffolk's butterflies and the habitats on which they depend. The appeal of this volume to the entomologist, naturalist and conservationist is assured. I believe too that it will encourage present and future naturalists to become keener observers and recorders, and to report their sightings. This will provide not only early notice of future declines, but perhaps also of the return to our County of a few of the species that so enriched its countryside in the past.

S. Beaufoy

ACKNOWLEDGEMENTS

THE SUFFOLK BUTTERFLY SURVEY (1983-1985) was from the beginning a Suffolk Naturalists' Society project, generously sponsored by Associated Tyre Specialists and the World Wildlife Fund, U.K. We are most grateful to the Society for unwavering support, and the considerable financial commitment which has enabled the results of the Survey to be published. Incoming records were channelled through the Ipswich Museum and Suffolk Biological Records Centre, and we thank Mr. J.G.R. Bevan (Director of Recreation and Amenities), Mr. A.G. Hatton (Curator, Ipswich Museums) and Mr. M.N. Sanford (Supervisor, Suffolk Biological Records Centre) for offering these facilities. Mrs. C.A. Green and Mr. J.R Martin, Secretary and Treasurer respectively, of the Suffolk Naturalists' Society have been responsible for the smooth running of the pre-publication sales.

It would have been impossible to produce the distribution maps without the records provided by local societies, and the hundreds of naturalists who took part in the Survey. Our sincere thanks to everyone and especially the principal recorders for their time and commitment. For the generous loan of books and periodicals we thank Mr. B.P.L. Higgs (British Butterfly Conservation Society), Mr. P.J. Trett, Mr. D.R. Moore, and Mr. S. Beaufoy, and for help with library services, Miss J.M. Harvey, Miss P. Gilbert and Ms. A. Jones (British Museum, Natural History), and Miss S. McElholm (Suffolk County Information and Library Service). For records and access to museum collections we thank Mrs. Humphreys-Jones (University Museum of Zoology, Cambridge), Mrs. K.M. Rowland (Colchester and Essex Museum), and Dr. A.G. Irwin (Castle Museum, Norwich). Messrs. P.T. Harding and B. Eversham of the Biological Records Centre, Monks Wood, and Mr. R.D. Sutton (British Butterfly Conservation Society) have made available the Suffolk records on their files, and Messrs. C. Garrett-Jones, A.L. Bull, G.J. Burton, W.S. George, A.E. Aston, H.E. Jenner, S. Beaufoy, R.F.A Eley and the late Mr. H.E. Chipperfield have been a great help with historical data.

It is not possible to acknowledge individually all the farmers and landowners who have allowed us access to land in their charge, but we would especially like to thank the Earl of Iveagh (Elveden Estate) and the Duke of Grafton (Euston Estate), and their respective managers, Messrs. W.M. Sloan and R.G.E. Starling.

It was difficult to select the plates from the large number of quality photographs sent for consideration. The source of the original photographs is acknowledged with each plate. Dr. G.D. Heathcote, and Messrs. A. Watchman, R. Barnett, E. Parsons and R.A.D. Markham have made very useful criticism of earlier drafts of the text; Mrs. E.M. Hyde, Miss C.M. McElholm, and Mr. E. Parsons have assisted with the proof-reading, and Mrs. J.M. Pratt and Mr. R.E. Clarke have helped considerably with the long and tedious work preparing the maps. Thanks also to Mrs. D.K. Faulkner who has patiently typed the various drafts and final manuscript.

6

Principal Recorders

Dr. A. Beaumont	J.A Foster	T.W. & L.G. Palmer
R. Beecroft	J.H. Grant	E. Parsons
T.J. Bennett	A.C. Hubbard	T.C. Rednall
M. Burnside	S.J. Hunt	A.K. Rivett
A.A. Butcher	D.C. Jardine	K. Scarff
R.E. Clarke	A.F. Leverett	C.S. Waller
M.T. Crawford	S.J. Ling	R. Walton
D. Croxon	E.C.B. Mares	A. Watchman
M.E. Dean	A.J. Morris	M.P. Wise
Ms. C.J. FitzGerald	C.R. Naunton	M.T. Wright

Records were also received from:

Ms. D.M. Abrahams, Rev. D.J.L. Agassiz, A. Aldous, R.M. Aldrich, Mrs. P. Aldred, Mr. & Mrs. P. Alexander, Mrs. Y.M. Amoss, R.W. Andrews, F.B.S. Antram, M. Austin, S. Babbs, Mrs. C. Bacon, Mrs. D. Baker, D.N. Bakewell, J.D. Bakewell, J.P. Balfour, Mr. F.G. Barcock, Dr. L.E. Barnes, H. Barnett, R.J. Barnett, Mrs. Barrett, Miss L.E. Bartrum, N.N. Beach, J. Beard, S. Beaufoy, Ms. F. Beaumont, P.A. Belden, Ms. E. Bell, Mr. & Mrs. R. Bennett, Mrs. S. Berry, J. Biglin, Mr. Bisphan, Miss J. Blackler, R. Blackler, T.A. Blount, E. Boggis, Mrs. B. Booker, T. Booker, Mrs. N.N. Bowen, P. Bowler, P.G. Boxhall, M. Bray, R.F. Bretherton, R.S. Briggs, Dr. C.R. Bristow, Mrs. B. Brock, Ms. S. Brown, T.K. Brown, Mrs. E. Bruce, A.L. Bull, Mrs. B. Burge, S.J. Burnell, G.J. Burton, D. Butcher, S. Butcher, D.J. Butters, Mrs. L.G. Calvesbert, S. Carruthers, M. Cass, Ms. S. Cass, Mrs. J.I. Casswell, W. Cattermole, H. Cavanagh, Mrs. M. Chamberlain, Mrs. B. Chandler, Mrs. L. Charlton, T. Charlton, Ms. N. Chapman, Mr. Chinery, H.E. Chipperfield, Mrs. J.P. Clarke, Ms. R.T. Clark, Mr. & Mrs. M. Claydon, J. Coe, N. Coe, H. Colby, A. Collier, B. Collins, Miss E. Collins, Miss D. Cooper, J. Cooper, J.M. Cooper, Mrs. R. Cooper, Misses B. & R. Copinger Hill, R. Copping, J. Cramp, Mr. & Mrs. T. Craven, Rev. N.L. Cribb, R. Crouch, D. Crowe, Ms. J. Cubey, P.D. Cutmore, Mr. Danison, R.J. Darrah, A. Davis, M.G. Davis, J.J. Davy, Mr. & Mrs. G.A. Day, Mrs. E. Dickson, A. Diebel, J.W. Digby, R, Dixon, O.G. Douglas, Mrs. M. Dowie, J. Drake, Mrs. E. Dunsdon, D.W. Durst, R.C. Dyson, A. Easton, H. Easton, Mrs. J.W.S. Edmundson, P.J. Edwards, Dr. E.A. Ellis, S.H. Evans, M.J. Everett, C. Eyre, K. Fairclough, Mrs. S.M. Fawcett, J.L. Fenn, M.J. Flack, A. Fordham, Miss K.H. Forwood, Mrs. R. Foster, Dr. W.A. Foster, Wing Commander F.J. French, G.M. French, J.W. Frost, G. Fussel, R.W. Gardiner, K.W. Garrod, W.S. George, M.V.V. Germain, Miss Gladwell, P. Gondris, G. Goodey, Mrs. S. Goodrich, R. Gouldby, M.F. Gould, M. Gower, P. Grant, K.J. Green, M.S. Green, S. Green, R.J. Greengrass, Lady J. Gwatkin, E.C.M. Haes, J. Haggar, Mrs. H.M. Hall, M.R. Hall, P. Hall, J. Hammersley, S. Hannant, M.M. Hards, Mrs. D. Harris, Mrs. A. Hart, R.F. Hartley, S.R. Hatch, D. Haylock, Mrs. Hazell, J. Heath, C.J.P. Heazell, Ms. L. Heggarty, S.K. Hellings, Dr. & Mrs. P.J. Helliwell, D. Hermon, C.R. Heseltine, Mrs. K. Hill, Dr. C.J. Hitch, R.N. Hobbs, T.J. Holtzer, J. Honeybone, Ms. I. Hood, Mrs. M. Hoy, Mrs. J. Hubbard, W. Hubbard, Mrs. G. Hunter, T. Hutton, Mrs. J. Huxley, Mrs. E.M. Hyde, P. Hyre, Mrs. Izzard, P. Jackson, Mr. Jacobs, H.E. Jenner, Mrs. B. Johnson, E. Jones, M.L. Jones, P.J. Jones, Mrs. E.K. Keane, Mrs. K. Keer, I.J. Killeen, D.P.T. Kines, Mr. & Mrs. M. King, S. King, Miss M.A. Kitchen, Mr. & Mrs. E. Kitson, W. Last, Mrs. S. Laverton, P. Lawson, B. Lawton, A.S. Lazenby, P. Leah, B. Lees, H.J. Lee, W.E. Lemmon, Mrs. G.R. Letts, A. Leutscher, G.P. List, Ms. K. Lloyd, R.A. Luff, B. Lumsden, R.H. Marchant, Ms. K. Mares, M.C. Marsh, R.V.A. Marshall, R. Martin, N. Mason, G.W. Maybury, Major W. Mayhew, Dr. P. McAnulty, Rev. H. Mead, Mrs. N. Meadows, D. Miller, N. Miller, J. Mills, E. Milne-Redhead, Mr Milton, D. Mitchell, D.R. Moore, J.L. Moore, Mrs. J.R. Moore, P. Moore, Mrs. A. Morgan, D. Morrison, Miss E. Mortimer, Miss P. Mould, A.J. Mowles, N. Muddeman, W.R. Mummery, C.R. Munford, P.W. Murphy, R.J. Mynott, D.R. Nash, J. & B. Neale, M. O'Brien, D.W. Ockleton, G, Oram, K.J. Orpe, D.M.S. Orr, G. Padfield, C. Page, A.R.J. Paine, T. Pankhurst, Mrs. Parker, O.B. Parker, Mrs. J. Parsons, J. Partridge, Mrs. Partridge, Miss J.R. Pask, E.W. Patrick, W.H. Payn, D.F. Pearsons, G. Peck, T.N.D. Peet, Miss G. Perkins, R.T. Perkins, R. Petley-Jones, H. Philbrick, C.W. Pierce, Mrs. S. Pim, Mrs. O. de Pinto, A.K. Piotrowski, D.J. Piotrowski, M.S. Piotrowski, S.P. Piotrowski, A. Pope, J. Pope, Ms. M. Powell, T. Proctor, Miss Pryke, Mrs. Pryke, D. Purches, Mrs. S. Pye, Miss B.M. Quilter, P. Quinn, Mrs. D. Radley, J.L. Raincock, B. Ranner, G. C. Raphael, Mrs. C. Rayner, J.R. Read, S. Read, D.A. Reilly, Mrs. S. Reynolds, H. Ricks, Mrs. M. Ridge, R. Roach, Mr. & Mrs. F. Roberts, F. Robinson, E.V. Rogers, K.S. Rodgers, J. Rolfe, A. Rowe, Mr. & Mrs. M.W. Rowland, B. Rowney, Mrs. J.M. Rudderham, M.A. Rufus, R.P. Ryan, Ms. M.E. Ryan, J.C. Sadler, K. Scarff, P.J. Schwind, J. Shackles, Miss V.J. Sheldrake, T.M. Shipp, F.W. Simpson, Mrs. A. Smith, Prof. C.C. Smith, Mrs. J.M. Smith, R.C. Southgate, Mrs. C. Steel, P. Steggall, J. Stevens, Mr. & Mrs. R. Stewart, H.L.G. Stroyan, P. Sutherland, Mrs. A. Sutton, R.D. Sutton, R. Swindin, Mrs. E. Szlichcinska, D. Tallis, M.C. & Mrs. A. Taylor, Ms. G.L. Taylor, W. Taylor, Dr. J.A. Thomas, B. Thompson, D. Thurkettle, Lieut.-Col. J.F. Todhunter, Mrs. B. Tooley, J.W. Tooley, A. Toone, T. Townsend, F.M. Trimble, H.G. Turner, J.A. Turner, K. Turner, Mrs. A. Upson, W. Urwin, Mrs. R. van der Does, Mrs. D. van Zwanenberg, Mrs. I.M. Vaughan, J.C. Wakerley, Mrs. A. Ware, Dr. M.S. Warren, R.B. Warren, Mrs. J.E. Watchman, R. Waters, A. Watson, Mrs. B. Way, J. Wearne, B.D. Webberley, Mrs. M. Wells, S. Went, Mr. & Mrs. A. Westcott, Mrs. J.E. West, Miss C. Wheeler, P.G.H. Wilson, B.J. Wingrove, T. Woodward, P.S. Wooler, R.J. Woolnough, I. Wynne, D.A. Young, Mrs. Young.

The Authors: Howard Mendel (left), Steve Piotrowski (right).

(East Anglian Daily Times)

INTRODUCTION

MANY INSECT SPECIES are declining, but it is usually only the specialist entomologist or collector that is any the wiser. Public awareness and concern for the fate of Britain's butterflies is better developed, and increasing as a result of media coverage and initiatives such as the 1981-82 "Butterfly Year". Suffolk was at one time amongst the best counties for butterflies in Britain, a stronghold for species such as the Large Tortoiseshell and White Admiral. The warnings of a decline began to sound in the late 1950's and early 1960's, but it is only with hindsight that real declines and extinctions can be separated from periodic fluctuations.

We decided to launch the Suffolk Butterfly Survey in 1982, on realising how few species we had actually seen in the County. It was tempting to dismiss the tales of past "times of plenty", as merely symptoms of the "good old days" syndrome, but how right they have proved to be. Since the War, Suffolk has been at the centre of the agricultural revolution, and we have lost butterfly habitats as a result of changes in agricultural practices, afforestation and urban development. Butterflies are a popular group of insects because they are so attractive, but their decline is not to be regretted for this alone. It is a good indication of what is happening to the many less obvious but equally important elements of our fauna.

8

THE COUNTY OF SUFFOLK

THE GENTLY undulating landscape of Suffolk rises to no more than a mere 420ft near Elms Farm, Depden. From this "high ground" in the south-west of the County the countryside falls to the fenland of the north-west, and more gradually across central Suffolk to the coast, and the most easterly point of Great Britain at Lowestoft Ness. There are approximately 50 miles of coastline. The principal landscape features are the river valleys, as there are no prominent hills. To the north, Suffolk is separated from Norfolk by the River Waveney and Little Ouse, and to the south the River Stour forms the border with Essex. The western border with Cambridgeshire follows the River Lark and tributaries for half its length.

Suffolk is a rural county of scattered villages and wide areas of arable farmland. The main centres of population are in the river valleys or along the coast, and the most highly developed area is Ipswich at the head of the Orwell Estuary. Although many of the County's towns and villages are expanding, urban spread is most intensive in the south-east. The once small seaside town of Felixstowe is developing as a port and villages such as Martlesham Heath, Capel St. Mary and Brantham are now approaching the size of small towns. The Suffolk landscape is changing, and since the Second World War at an ever increasing pace, and there are few habitats that have remained untouched.

Figure 1.
Towns and large villages.

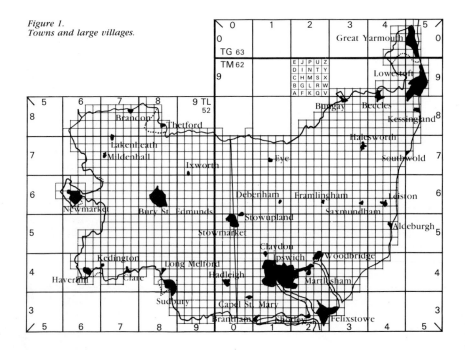

CLIMATE

IT IS GENERALLY ACCEPTED that climate often determines the maximum possible range of a butterfly, either directly or by limiting the range of acceptable larval foodplants. The climate of Suffolk is more continental than most parts of Britain, and both diurnal and seasonal ranges of temperature are more extreme, as would be expected. The frequency of warm summer days and the maximum temperatures attained are generally well above those of more westerly counties, and Suffolk enjoys above average daily total hours of sunshine. Winters tend to be colder than in most areas of lowland Britain, and in the Brecklands ground frosts are unusually frequent. Santon Downham recorded ground frosts in each month of the year between 1960-1964 (Duffey, 1976).

Suffolk has little rainfall, less than 25″ p.a. over much of the area. The coastal belt is particularly dry, and it is often warm and clear in the south-east of the County when it is showery inland. The heaviest rainfall normally occurs in the summer and autumn months, between July and October, and spring and early summer are usually dry, though cold easterly and north-easterly winds are often associated with mist and fog.

GEOLOGY AND SOILS

THE GEOLOGICAL STRUCTURE of Suffolk is comparatively simple and the surface rocks are of no great age — geologically speaking, that is. The foundation of Chalk beneath the whole area was formed up to 70 million years ago, and inclines gently to the south-east. It is for the most part covered by younger strata, only surfacing in the west and where it has been exposed in the valleys around Needham Market, Sudbury and Haverhill.

The Thanet and Reading Beds, and London Clay of the Eocene Period, above the Chalk, do not feature prominently in Suffolk but may be seen in the lower valleys of the Rivers Stour, Orwell, Deben and Brett, and on the coast at Felixstowe and Bawdsey. Various sands and gravels of the "Crag" series, with some clays, cover the London Clay in East Suffolk. These often highly fossiliferous strata forming the soft, crumbling cliffs north of Bawdsey and at Southwold, were deposited between ½ and 3½ million years ago. Much of the Chalk, the Eocene beds of the Tertiary and these younger sands and gravels have either been removed or obscured by glacial action. The stiff Boulder Clay and the glacial sands and gravels of Breckland and East Suffolk cover about two-thirds of the County, and are largely responsible for the topography and landscape typical of the area. Later deposits include the coastal sand and shingle accumulations, and fenland and valley peats and alluvium.

The surface geology determines the soil types. The Chalk in the west has developed typically thin, well-drained calcareous soils and highly calcareous subsoils, contrasting sharply with the nearby thick black peat soils of Fenland. In Breckland the thickness of the mantle of sand determines the soil type and acidity, but the influence of the chalk is strong over much of the area. A stiff chalky or stony Boulder Clay covers

Figure 2. Simplified geological map of Suffolk. (Jonny M. Stone)

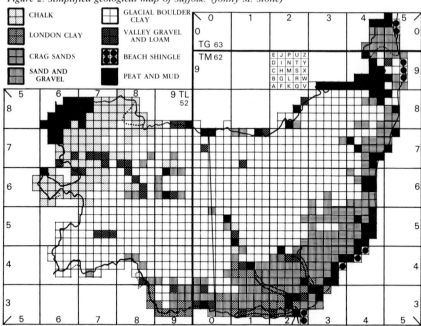

most of central Suffolk, giving way to a complex of well-drained sand and gravel soils towards the coastal plain.

The different soil types develop characteristic floras and are associated with distinct patterns of land use. Some of our butterfly species depend on larval foodplants, the distributions of which are determined by geology and soil type. However, in Suffolk, land use has proved to be a far more significant factor affecting butterfly distribution, especially in recent years.

SUFFOLK BUTTERFLY HABITATS
WOODLAND

THERE SEEMS LITTLE DOUBT that, except for the fenland, river flood plains and certain coastal areas, woodland once covered most of Suffolk. By medieval times the huge woodland tracts had been broken up and "coppice with standards" management became established. With this form of management the underwood or shrub layer is cut for hurdles, fences, poles and firewood on a regular cycle, and the standard trees felled as required for timber. This pattern of management continued, little changed, to the 19th century. Other areas of woodland were managed as parkland and may also date from medieval times. These are characterised by their ancient pollard or standard oaks; Helmingham and Staverton Parks are two examples.

Since medieval times woodlands have seldom been left to follow their natural succession, but have been changed and exploited by man. The regular cutting of small areas of underwood promoted a rich ground flora which included the foodplants required by the larvae of some of our now long extinct butterflies, such as the Heath Fritillary. Management kept the tracks and rides open, and this was probably as important for the butterflies as the coppicing itself. In the 18th and 19th centuries the woodlands were linked by copses, groves and tree-lined lanes, but many are now islands surrounded by arable land, and populations of the less mobile butterflies are more isolated than ever they were in the past. The distribution of woodlands today (Fig. 3), with the exception of the large conifer blocks, presents a pattern of well-scattered small areas.

In Suffolk the woodlands of the south-east with a higher density of standard oaks were the ones famous for butterflies, and Beaufoy (1945) wrote, *"We doubt whether many spots are now left in England where so many kinds of Rhopalocera [butterflies] are observable together as the Bentley woods near Ipswich."* Coppicing began to decline in the last century and few woods were still managed in this way by the Second World War, but we can see no obvious correlation between the rapid decline of Suffolk's woodland butterflies in the 1950's and the history of coppice management. Their disappearance was as complete in woodland with a good history of management, as in that which had been long neglected. During the late 1940's and 1950's many of our ancient woodlands were grubbed out or clear felled and replanted with conifers. Between the Wars, and more especially after the Second World War, many of the Oak standards were removed and this is thought to have contributed to the demise of Suffolk's woodland butterflies. The return to so-called "coppice" management in recent years, cutting large areas

Ancient coppice woodland with standards — Cambridgeshire.

(B. Sawford)

at a time and leaving the minimum of standards lest they shade out and reduce the value of the underwood crop, offers little hope for the butterflies.

Much of the deciduous woodland today is managed for game preservation, and some of the woodlands in north-east Suffolk were planted in the 18th and 19th centuries, on former arable or heathland, specifically for that purpose. It has been argued that intensive pheasant rearing may have been responsible for the decline of some of the woodland butterflies. Poplar plantations are a common sight in Suffolk along rivers and streams, grown for the match industry, and those in the north-west hold large populations of Orange Tips, Ringlets and Speckled Woods. In other areas there are woodlands which have developed naturally from scrub.

It will come as a surprise to many to learn that whilst the afforestation of the Breckland and the Sandlings has ruined large areas of heathland, the forests with their wide fire-breaks and well-managed tracks and ride systems are excellent for butterflies. They hold many of the heathland and heathland edge species such as Grayling, Small Heath, Brown Argus and Small Copper, support almost all Suffolk's remaining colonies of White Admiral and Dingy Skipper, and have proved suitable for the return to Suffolk of the Speckled Wood. Where there are Oak screens, good colonies of Purple Hairstreaks are often found. Many of the coniferised ancient woodlands are also very good for butterflies, again because of their wide, well-maintained ride systems with diverse floras. With the exception of the Purple and perhaps White-letter Hairstreaks, there are virtually no truly woodland butterflies left in Suffolk's deciduous woodlands.

Ancient woodland re-planted with conifers — Assington Thicks.

(H. Mendel)

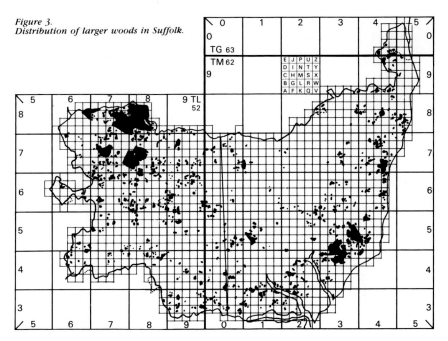

Figure 3.
Distribution of larger woods in Suffolk.

GRASSLAND

GRASSLANDS OF ONE SORT OR ANOTHER form an important element of many other habitats, including woodland and heathland which are described in separate sections. Here we consider "pioneer habitats" created following disturbance by man, as well as semi-natural grassland types.

Pits and Quarries

Suffolk is dotted with pits and quarries, and man's efforts to extract useful materials from the ground date back some 4000 years to the Neolithic flint mines of Breckland. In more recent times the Chalk has been quarried for agricultural lime, cement and flints for building, the London Clay and later brickearths for brickmaking and the Boulder Clay for cement. "Crag" has been used for building stone, road material, and fertiliser, the phosphatic coprolites once forming the basis of a local industry. There are also sand and gravel pits producing aggregate for concrete. The 19th century was the heyday for small pits and very many villages dug their own local deposits of brickearths or loams. It was not uncommon for large farms to have marl pits, or a small crag or gravel pit for surfacing roads and tracks.

Many of the older pits and quarries are filled with dense scrub or have been reclaimed, and are poor butterfly habitats. Others, especially the chalk pits, have developed characteristic open turf on the poor, well-drained soils, and are rich with pioneer plant species such as Bird's-foot Trefoil, Kidney Vetch and other larval food plants. The sheltered bottoms and terraces on their south-facing sides act as suntraps with very favourable microclimates. Old chalk and sand pits support colonies of Brown Argus and Dingy Skipper as well as the more common grassland species such as Wall, Grayling, Small Heath and Common Blue.

Pits and quarries have been seen as scars on the landscape, and all too often in recent years have been used for refuse disposal. This was the fate of one of the most interesting chalk pits in the County, near Little Blakenham. Many of the larger pits in the river valleys and Breckland are left flooded and stocked for fishing, or are used for water sports.

Meadows and Pastures

The water meadows of the valley bottoms and pastures often associated with woodland, once features of the Suffolk countryside, have virtually disappeared. The Marsh Fritillary was an early casualty, but from the 1960's populations of the Dingy and Grizzled Skippers have crashed.

Since the decline of the working horse and the general move away from livestock to intensive arable farming, pasture land has become a scarce commodity. Fields are ploughed right up to the woodland edges and any narrow grassy strips that remain suffer the effects of crop spray drift. Wet meadows are drained or "improved" to give a better hay crop, and small uneconomic areas quickly develop scrub, especially since the advent of myxomatosis. Some of the wider woodland rides now provide the best examples of meadow land, and where these are cut annually or heavily grazed by rabbits, many of the common grassland butterflies prosper.

Roadside Verges and Hedgerows

Roadside verges are becoming increasingly important refuges for grassland butterfly species, and in some areas provide a ribbon of suitable habitat through an otherwise arable "desert". In such places the wider the verges the better for the butterflies, and already too many have been whittled away to a width of a few feet or less, and suffer the full effects of toxic sprays used on the adjacent arable land. Roadside cuttings often produce a most favourable butterfly habitat, the well-drained subsoils developing sparse grassland with early colonising species such as Bird's-foot Trefoil, the larval foodplant of the Common Blue and Dingy Skipper.

Verges will soon develop scrub vegetation and become less suitable for butterflies unless they are well grazed or occasionally mown. In these days of financial restraint, cutting is less regular than it used to be and it is likely that many verges will be lost as grassland habitat. How often and when a verge is cut, also helps to determine how good it is for butterflies. Few browns are found on verges mown in July, and Orange Tip larvae are destroyed by a June cut.

The best verges for butterflies are usually those of a moderate width, perhaps with a ditch, and backed by a good hedgerow with scattered mature trees, or running into a woodland edge. Many such verges and flowery waysides with Knapweeds, Field Scabious and Thistles are still to be found along country lanes and farm tracks. These are ideal not only for true grassland species, the browns and skippers, but also for the woodland edge butterflies: the Orange Tip, Holly Blue and Comma. However, the verges and banks of the main trunk roads are also of interest.

The coarse grassland along most of the length of the new A45 is ideal for the Essex Skipper which literally swarms in suitable areas, and it is likely that the spread of this species in recent years has been along such verges. The only "nature reserve" specifically for butterflies in Suffolk is in fact a wide verge, protected by agreement between the Suffolk County Council and the Suffolk Trust for Nature Conservation, for the Essex Skipper, thought to be rare in the County before the Butterfly Survey. Such protected verges championed by Mr. E. Milne-Redhead of the Suffolk Trust are invaluable.

Railway Tracks

The embankments and cuttings associated with both disused railways and those still in service provide a butterfly habitat similar to roadside verges. The herb-rich grassland interspaced with short grazed turf on the usually poor soils is soon invaded by scrub if not managed, and becomes less valuable. In the days of steam, frequent fires prevented the encroachment of bramble and scrub.

Two stretches of disused line, at Lavenham and Hadleigh, have been purchased by the Local Authority and are maintained as nature reserve walks. In spite of management the grassland is losing to Blackthorn encroachment and a colony of Dingy Skippers seems to have been lost. Other stretches of disused track warrant "reserve" status. Parts of the old line between Lowestoft and Gorleston, some of which are being filled with refuse, the disused track through Fritton Warren, sections between Bury St. Edmunds and Thetford, Long Melford and Haverhill, and further stretches of the Bentley to Hadleigh and Bury to Lavenham lines are some of the many lengths which are excellent for butterflies.

Chalk Grassland

This is a very restricted habitat in spite of the extensive beds of Chalk beneath the whole of Suffolk. The best examples of chalk grassland are found in the Newmarket area and the Gipping Valley, but some of the chalkpits of the Breckland and the river valleys have also developed good chalk floras. Newmarket Heath, which straddles the Suffolk/ Cambridgeshire border, was at one time by far the best butterfly habitat, but most of Suffolk's chalk grassland species — Silver-spotted Skipper, Adonis Blue and Marbled White — were lost before the turn of the century. The Chalk Hill Blue lasted only a little longer.

The Coast and Estuaries

The mile upon mile of sand and shingle along Suffolk's uniform shoreline between Landguard Point and Gorleston, belies the complexity of the coastal habitats. This sand and shingle is derived from the soft coastal cliffs at Covehithe, Dunwich, Bawdsey and elsewhere and is deposited in huge banks. The most extensive by far is Orfordness, a bleak spit some nine miles long. The crumbling cliffs and sand and shingle banks develop a fascinating flora of salt tolerant pioneer species, including grasses supporting populations of Wall and Small Heath, and Bird's-foot Trefoil with Common Blues. The shingle deposition has closed some estuaries, forming brackish meres, the broads of Easton, Covehithe and Benacre.

There are dunes between Sizewell and Dunwich and beneath the cliffs at Kessingland, and grassy under-cliffs in areas of deposition well protected from the waves by steep beaches.

There are still extensive salt marshes in Suffolk, although many have been reclaimed as grazing meadows. These fields are protected from tidal flooding by artificial walls and banks, which are usually covered by grass. Small and Essex Skippers thrive on these banks, and Wall and Small Heath may also be found in plenty.

Many migrant butterflies remain in the region of the coast, and woodland and heathland species are sometimes seen there. It is not uncommon to find Purple Hairstreaks on Oaks overhanging the crumbling cliffs at Easton and Benacre. Orange Tips on the other hand appear to be scarce in the immediate vicinity of the coast and larger estuaries.

Grassy cliffs and under-cliffs — Kessingland Beach.   *(H. Mendel)*

HEATHLAND

SUFFOLK'S BARREN HEATHLANDS were formed as a result of man's use, and often misuse, of a more fertile landscape. Forest clearance, followed by a system of agriculture causing impoverishment of the soil, was the usual pattern of development. Neolithic man started the clearance of the open Oak forest land some 5000 years ago in the Breckland of the north-west. Plots of land are thought to have been cultivated until the already poor glacial soils became exhausted, and domestic animals prevented the development of scrub, and re-growth of forest. Sheep grazed these heaths from Roman times, and huge rabbit warrens were established in the Middle Ages. Extensive inland sand dunes developed as the structure of the soil broke down, but the most extensive area of these was destroyed in the 1940's when Lakenheath Airbase was built.

Breckland heaths are a mixture of fine, herb-rich turf, Sand Sedge, Ling and open sand areas. They have a unique flora, especially rich where the effects of the underlying chalk are felt, and it is interesting that, unlike the coastal heaths, there is almost no Bell Heather. Small Coppers, Common Blues, Small and Essex Skippers abound, but less common species such as Grayling and Dingy Skipper are more restricted in distribution. The once common Silver-studded Blue has now disappeared from Suffolk Breckland.

In the 20th century scientific agricultural methods have enabled extensive areas of the Breck to be reclaimed as arable farmland, and there has been considerable afforestation. It is estimated that of the 54,000 acres of Breckland heath in Suffolk and neighbouring Norfolk in 1880, only 6,600 acres remained by 1968 (Duffey, 1976). There are still extensive areas at Cavenham, Icklingham, Thetford, Elveden and Lakenheath, and interesting tracts along the wider forest rides and fire-breaks.

The Sandlings heaths of coastal Suffolk between Ipswich and Lowestoft totalled some 10,000 acres in the mid-19th century, but huge areas have been reclaimed for agriculture, afforested or lost to airport construction. During the Wars many acres were ploughed in an attempt to increase national output, but some of these have been allowed to revert to heathland. The major losses have occurred since the 1920's, when it

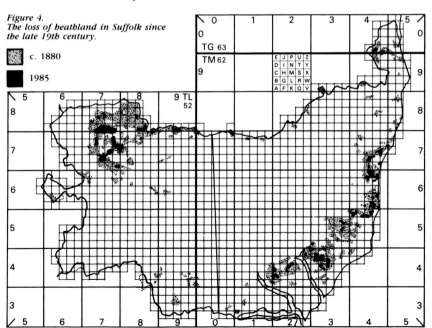

Figure 4.
The loss of heathland in Suffolk since the late 19th century.

c. 1880

1985

Sandlings — Sutton Heath.   *(R. Beecroft)*

was discovered that lime added to the soil improved the fertility, and at about the same time the Forestry Commission started to buy land for afforestation.

The Sandlings heaths were traditionally grazed by sheep and later by rabbits, and many suffered badly from the encroachment of Gorse, Bracken, Birch, and Pine after the outbreak of myxomatosis in the 1950's. No doubt species such as the Green Hairstreak have benefited, but the Silver-studded Blue and Grayling must have suffered. More recently urban development of this land, described as "low grade agricultural" by the planners, has taken its toll. South-east Suffolk has been the worst affected, with planning permission given for the development of Nacton Heath, Fox's Heath, Warren Heath, Bixley Heath and Martlesham Heath. This has badly affected the Silver-studded Blue, as well as the more common heathland butterflies.

Outside the Sandlings and Breckland are other interesting areas of heathland. Newton Green, now a golf course, is the last remaining area of the heathlands of south-west Suffolk (Chatters, 1985), and over the past 200 years heathland in this part of the County has dwindled from 500 to 10 acres. Other areas of heathland are found along the Waveney Valley and include Wortham Ling, Stuston Common, and remnants in the Fritton area of Lothingland.

Table 1. Suffolk Butterflies 1980-1985 — habitat preference summary

	WOODLAND		GRASSLAND		HEATHLAND	
	Conifer	Deciduous	Woodland edge & Hedgerow	Open Sites	Breckland	Sandlings
Small Skipper	+	+	+	*	*	*
Essex Skipper	+	+	+	*	*	*
Large Skipper	*	*	*	+	+	+
Dingy Skipper	*			+	*	
Grizzled Skipper						
Clouded Yellow	+	+	+	+	+	+
Brimstone	*	*	*	+	+	+
Large White	*	*	*	*	*	*
Small White	*	*	*	*	*	*
Green-veined White	*	*	*	+	+	+
Orange Tip	*	*	*	+	+	+
Green Hairstreak	*				*	*
Purple Hairstreak	+	*				*
White-letter Hairstreak		*	*			
Small Copper	*	+	+	*	*	*
Silver-studded Blue						*
Brown Argus	*			*	*	
Common Blue	+	+	+	*	*	*
Holly Blue	+	*	*			
White Admiral	*	+				
Red Admiral	*	*	*	+	+	+
Painted Lady	+	+	+	*	*	*
Small Tortoiseshell	+	+	*	*	+	+
Large Tortoiseshell		*				
Peacock	+	*	*	+	+	+
Comma	*	*	*			
Speckled Wood	*	+		+		
Wall	+	+	+	*	+	+
Grayling	+			+	*	*
Gatekeeper	*	*	*	+	+	+
Meadow Brown	*	*	*	*	*	*
Small Heath	*	+	+	*	*	*
Ringlet	*	*	*			

* Greatest concentrations of a species.
+ Present regularly in small numbers.

WOODLAND *Conifer* — areas of plantation and coniferised ancient woodland with wide open rides and fire-breaks, often with deciduous screens.
Deciduous — ancient neglected coppice and secondary woodland.

GRASSLAND *Woodland Edge and Hedgerow* — sheltered often shaded sites usually with tall grasses.
Open Sites — grazed turf or sparse grassland in exposed situations or on thin soils after disturbance, and including much of the coastline.

HEATHLAND *Breckland* — North-west Suffolk.
Sandlings — East Suffolk.

HISTORY OF RECORDING

THE INFLUENCE OF THE Rev. William Kirby (1759-1850), for many years rector of Barham, on all branches of entomology in the early part of the 19th century can not be underestimated. Many prominent lepidopterists of the day visited his Barham parsonage, and it is to Kirby that Laetitia Jermyn (1788-1848) of Ipswich, dedicated the three editions of her *"Butterfly Collector's Vade Mecum"*, published between 1824 and 1836. These curious little volumes, the last in her married name Ford, list many Suffolk localities, including Benacre as a site for the Large Copper. An annotated copy of the 1827 edition known to Claude Morley, almost certainly inscribed by John Davey Hoy (1797-1839) of Stoke-by-Nayland, provides further valuable data on the butterflies of Suffolk in the early 19th century. At about the same time the Pagets (1834) catalogued the butterflies of north-east Suffolk in their *"Sketch of the Natural History of Yarmouth and its Neighbourhood."*

Not long after Kirby's death a *"List of Lepidoptera occurring in the County of Suffolk"* compiled by the Rev. Joseph Greene of Brandeston and Playford, assisted by the Rev. H. Harpur Crewe and C.R. Bree, both of Stowmarket, appeared in parts in Morris' Naturalist from 1857. This encouraged comment, and the following year R.B. Postans (1858) produced his list of *"Suffolk Lepidoptera"*. Many prominent lepidopterists collected in Suffolk during the second half of the 19th century and their notes and records appear regularly in the entomological journals. C.G. Barrett, A.H. Wrattislaw, W.M. Crowfoot, N.F. Hele, H. Lingwood, Garrett Garrett, H. Miller, W. Harwood, T. and J. Brown and F. Norgate are but a few of the many collectors of that era who made their records available to the Rev. E.N. Bloomfield (1827-1914), enabling him to publish his *"Lepidoptera of Suffolk"* in 1890. Many of the records also appeared in the standard works of the period, a few in Stainton (1857) and Morris (1857) and many more in Newman (1870-71). These have been quoted time and again over the years and are mostly accurate, but we have little confidence in those from *"Brandeston and Playford"* attributed to Joseph Greene in Newman.

"Additions to former List", the first supplement to Bloomfield's catalogue, appeared in 1900, adding the Niobe Fritillary to the Suffolk butterfly fauna. The Victoria County History, following soon after in 1911, contained little more than an outline of previously published data, and the next milestone was the formation of the Suffolk Naturalists' Society in 1929, by Claude Morley. A primary object was *"The publication of permanent Record, in reasoned sequence, of facts respecting the comparative past and present rarity of Animals and Plants in Suffolk"*, and the Transactions of the same year carried the *"Second Supplement"* to Bloomfield's *"Lepidoptera of Suffolk"*, compiled by Rev. A.P. Waller, and this added four butterfly species to the Suffolk list.

Regular notes and short papers on Suffolk's butterflies became a feature of the annual "Transactions" and by 1937 sufficient new data had been accumulated to warrant the publication of the Society's first

"Memoir"; the *"Final Catalogue of the Lepidoptera of Suffolk"*, edited by Claude Morley. Morley was a most energetic collector and cataloguer of all forms of insect life, and no single individual either before or after has added so much to our knowledge of Suffolk insects. An annotated copy of Bloomfield (1890) and various manuscript lists and jottings in the Society's archive at Ipswich Museum show that he was largely responsible for the section covering the butterflies, even though Dr. C.H.S. Vinter is given as "Recorder" for this group.

Morley's catalogue was termed "Final" because it included all lists from previous catalogues, and because at that time a subsequent publication in such detail seemed so improbable. The impetus to recording it gave meant that *"Addenda et Corrigenda"* were necessary the following year in the Transactions.

Over the years following, very many interesting papers, notes and observations appeared in the Transactions and Proceedings of the Suffolk Naturalists' Society, by the official Recorders, C.H.S. Vinter, C.G.M. de Worms, S. Beaufoy and H.E. Chipperfield; C. Morley, E.W. Platten, A.E. Aston, E.T. Goldsmith, P.J. Burton, F.W. Frohawk, M. Hocken, A. P. Waller, J.L. Moore, J. Goddard, W.S. George and many others.

In 1970 Mr. S. Beaufoy brought our knowledge of Suffolk butterflies up-to-date with his paper *"Suffolk Butterflies from 1945"*, giving the first indication of major declines, to be followed by *"A review of some butterflies and moths in Suffolk during the past fifty years"* by Baron C.G.M. de Worms (1979). Other local societies have also regularly published lists of butterflies found in their area, most notably the Lowestoft and North Suffolk Field Naturalists' Club, which has produced an annual report since 1946. The Suffolk Butterfly Survey has built on this long tradition of recording.

CONSERVATION

"There is no doubt that butterflies are dying out in this county. I do not mean that there will ever be no butterflies here, but that the ones you see will be merely the common kinds — the Whites and Browns and Blues, the plebs of the highways and hedges". (Morley, 1920).

OVER THE SIXTY-FIVE years since Morley made this prediction many species have been lost and others have become extremely local and rare. Excluding the three regular migrants unable to survive our winters, the Clouded Yellow, Red Admiral and Painted Lady, only 30 species of butterflies are found in Suffolk. This is if anything an exaggeration; of that 30 the Grizzled Skipper has not been definitely seen since 1979 and the Large Tortoiseshell is barely surviving. The change in status of Suffolk butterflies is summarised in Table 2. The appalling number of extinctions and severe declines is self evident.

The obvious reasons for many of these losses are discussed in more detail in other sections of this book. If a site is destroyed by urban development or agriculture, the butterflies will also be destroyed. More subtle changes of land management — changes in mowing regimes on grassland, application of fertilizers, cessation of grazing and the like — also have far reaching effects. The less mobile and less adaptable species, those with precise habitat requirements, are the first to suffer. Grizzled Skipper and Silver-studded Blue are good examples, because they depend on habitat in an early successional stage, and even quite small changes can result in local extinctions.

The influence of climate and weather is even more subtle. Few would argue that climate was not an important factor determining distribution, but it is very difficult to analyse the specific effects of its numerous components. It is even more difficult to see how these many variables work together, and with other environmental factors, especially in the short term. Means of rainfall and temperature are useful statistics, but it is far too simplistic to expect them to produce precise correlations with variations in butterfly numbers. Dennis (1977) provides a very good review and discussion of the various effects of climate. In the 1950's there was a period with temperatures below the long-term average and it would be surprising indeed if this did not contribute to the disappearance of some butterflies at that time. The distributions of the Pearl-bordered Fritillary, High Brown Fritillary and others have contracted nationally to the south and west in a way that makes it difficult to exclude climatic involvement.

Weather, the day by day manifestation of climate, also has its effects on butterfly populations, resulting in "good years" and "bad years" for different species. In 1984 the Small Tortoiseshell was scarce throughout the season, largely as a result of an early warm spell bringing butterflies out of hibernation, which was followed by a prolonged cold, wet period, resulting in failure of the first generation. The season by season variation in flight periods is normally attributed to weather. In the exceptional season of 1941, early White Admirals were flying with late Orange Tips

(Platten, 1941b) and late Grizzled Skippers with early Large Skippers (Morley, 1941). The weather also affects the levels of parasitism, predation and disease in butterfly populations, which undoubtedly cause periodic fluctuations in their numbers.

Myxomatosis was first reported in England in 1953 and in Suffolk later the same year at Easton Bavents (Haslam, 1955). Elveden estate game records show that bags of rabbits dropped from 19,839 in the 1953/54 season to a mere 401 in 1955/6 after the outbreak of myxomatosis, though they picked up a little in subsequent years (Cranbrook, 1958). The growth of rank vegetation after the demise of the rabbit was recognised in the early 1960's, and the resulting encroachment of scrub and Bracken on heathland is now well documented. It is also likely that the woodland flora was adversely affected and it is interesting that the decline of the woodland butterflies occurred in the 1950's. A coincidence perhaps?

It has often been said that over-zealous collectors have depleted our butterfly populations, but such statements are coloured by ethics and emotions. Species reduced to very low levels by other factors can be wiped out by unscrupulous collectors. Far too many people collect butterflies as other enthusiasts might collect stamps, and there has been an upsurge of dealers and butterfly "farms" to supply the demand. Although for the most part a relatively harmless pursuit, there is little knowledge to be gained through collecting British butterflies, unless they are taken in the course of some specific study, or in the case of rare migrants to prove a record. Collectors should follow the "Code for Insect Collecting" written by the Joint Committee for the Conservation of British Insects. Keen young entomologists with the urge to collect should be encouraged to turn their attentions to less well known insect groups where there is still much to be learned through collecting. An excellent discussion of the pros and cons of collecting British butterflies is given by Stubbs (1985).

Can anything be done to prevent further local extinctions before we are left with only "*the plebs of the highways and hedges*"? The County is reasonably well off for nature reserves: the Nature Conservancy Council manages large areas of Benacre, Walberswick, Blythburgh and Orfordness, the Royal Society for the Protection of Birds has reserves at Minsmere, Havergate and Wolves Wood near Hadleigh, and the Suffolk Trust for Nature Conservation controls a wealth of smaller reserves dotted across the County. Other organisations, the National Trust, Local Authorities and private individuals also maintain areas for nature conservation. However, nature reserves can only be seen as a part of the answer and butterfly losses from them have been as great as elsewhere. One of the problems is a lack of knowledge about the biology and behaviour of many of our species. There is still a tremendous amount to be learned from careful observation in the field, and until such basic information as foodplant preference and egg laying behaviour are better known, habitat management will be "hit and miss". Local knowledge from field studies is most important; because butterfly larvae will feed on a certain plant in captivity does not mean they will do so in the wild. Similarly the habitat requirements of a species in, for example, Wales will not necessarily hold good for the same species in Suffolk.

The fate of many of Suffolk's butterfly species lies with the farmers and landowners such as the Forestry Commission and Local Authorities. Again lack of basic data has been a problem, but at least we now know which of our species are declining, and where many of the remaining colonies are. During the course of the Butterfly Survey it has been heartening to meet a good many landowners and farmers who are not only interested in butterflies, but also want to know how to manage "rough" areas of their land to preserve them. Efforts should be made to protect remaining colonies of the rarer species by scheduling some of the more important areas as Sites of Special Scientific Interest, and by agreement with the owners of others.

Conservationists should object to the further development of important sites; if this only makes planning authorities more aware the next time, it will have been worthwhile. The digging up and physical movement of a habitat, out of the way of development, should not be looked upon as a conservation option. Even relatively simple ecosystems such as heathland are extremely complex, and it is naive to expect to move them bodily without serious damage. The fateful "move" of Warren Heath near Ipswich in an attempt to save the Silver-studded Blue failed dismally. Developers will be eager to believe that habitat moves are an option, and will be quite prepared to budget accordingly. No site will be safe.

Re-introductions, on the other hand, have often been successful, but should not be entered into lightly. Habitat fragmentation and isolation make it extremely unlikely that suitable areas will be colonised naturally by some of the more sedentary species. Introductions should not be carried out without the approval of the Nature Conservancy Council, and even then should be registered with the local and national Biological Records Centres. Thoughtless releases and secret re-introductions can wreak havoc with recording and monitoring programmes, and even now the status and history of some of Suffolk's butterflies is confused for this very reason. A strict code of practice is needed.

Rearing butterflies is now becoming an increasingly popular pastime, but there is always the question of what to do with the butterflies when they emerge. Release of stock in areas where a species is not already found is irresponsible. For those interested in seeing more butterflies in their immediate environs, it is far better to plant nectar flowers such as Buddleia, Michaelmas Daisies and Ice Plants, and perhaps also larval foodplants such as Holly and Ivy for the Holly Blue. "Butterfly gardening", as it has come to be called, is an interesting way of seeing more butterflies and there are several useful books devoted to the subject.

Table 2. The change in status of Suffolk butterflies

	EXTINCTIONS			Relative status of surviving species since 1960			
19th century	1900-1949	1950-1985	Severe Declines	Local Declines	Little Change	Increase
Silver-spotted Skipper	Swallowtail	Small Blue	Dingy Skipper	Orange Tip	Small Skipper	Essex Skipper
	Wood White	Purple Emperor	Grizzled Skipper	Green Hairstreak	Large Skipper	White Admiral*2
Black-veined White	Brown Hairstreak	Large Tortoiseshell*1	Silver-studded Blue	White-letter Hairstreak	Brimstone	Speckled Wood
Large Copper	Chalk Hill Blue	Small Pearl-bordered Fritillary	Brown Argus	Small Copper	Large White	
Adonis Blue	Duke of Burgundy Fritillary	Pearl-bordered Fritillary		Common Blue	Small White	
Mazarine Blue		High Brown Fritillary		Wall	Green-veined White	
Heath Fritillary	Marsh Fritillary	Dark Green Fritillary		Grayling	Purple Hairstreak	
Marbled White		Silver-washed Fritillary		Small Heath	Holly Blue	
				Ringlet	Small Tortoiseshell	
					Peacock	
					Comma	
					Gatekeeper	
					Meadow Brown	
7 Species	6 Species	8 Species	4 Species	9 Species	13 Species	3 Species

*1 The Large Tortoiseshell all but disappeared in the 1950's, but recent sightings could be interpreted as survival at very low population levels.

*2 There are indications that the White Admiral is increasing, but it is too soon to be certain.

THE SUFFOLK BUTTERFLY SURVEY

A NUMBER OF PUBLICATIONS over the years have attempted to describe and review the distribution of butterflies in Suffolk, based on the personal experience of a small number of lepidopterists. Much of the data has already been incorporated into the excellent national distribution maps prepared by the Biological Records Centre, Monks Wood (Heath, *et al.*, 1984). However, because their recording unit is necessarily large (a 10 km square), local patterns are often lost. The Suffolk Butterfly Survey was the first attempt to systematically record the whole County in detail and so provide base-line data on all the butterfly species. It was apparent from the beginning that despite the tremendous expertise within the County, the number of active lepidopterists would be insufficient to achieve the desired level of coverage. It was therefore necessary to involve as many interested members of the general public as possible.

Appeals were made through the local press and T.V., and the newsletters of the major relevant local societies: the Suffolk Naturalists' Society, Suffolk Trust for Nature Conservation and Suffolk Ornithologists' Group. At the same time a meeting was held to solicit the help of the County's more expert lepidopterists. The majority of less experienced volunteers wanted to record their gardens and perhaps a few other local sites, and were provided with an easy to use "Garden Recorder's Pack" complete with the necessary instructions. Our more experienced recorders were issued with a larger and slightly more sophisticated "Recorder's Pack" designed for less intensive coverage of many more sites. The balance worked well, and it was only on recalling the recorders' packs after the first year of the Survey in the winter of 1983 that we fully realized the value of "in depth" recording of a single site, even by a relatively inexperienced observer. Our initial worries about the accuracy of identification proved unfounded. The majority of "rogue" records were easy to spot and anything doubtful was rejected. From season to season butterflies have relatively constant flight periods and records outside these were closely scrutinised. Confusion between similar species could also be spotted and garden lists with records for Large White, but none for Small or Green-veined Whites, for example, were suspect. It is likely that far more good records have been rejected than bad records accepted.

All records from the first year of the Survey were plotted with others known to us dating back to 1980, and issued to our 100 staunchest supporters as a *"Provisional Atlas"* incorporating further recording sheets. "Garden Packs" were used unchanged throughout the Survey. The *"Provisional Atlas"* gave the Survey new impetus as recorders went out to fill "white holes." By the end of the second season's fieldwork we were near to achieving our target of complete coverage. This was effectively the end of the two year survey and during 1985 the small team that continued for the final year were able to visit the few remaining squares to achieve "coverage", and also spend time checking suspected sites for rarer species. Although the maps are plotted by tetrads (blocks of four 1 km squares) the data has been gathered by 1 km squares, and nearly all records are from named localities and have precise dates.

Over 85% of the records in the most recent date class were gathered in the two "official" Survey years, 1983-84. Rapid declines are easily masked by a recording period of say 10 or 15 years, and it was for this reason that we decided on a short but intensive survey. The disadvantage of this is that the rarest species may be missed, and the results are more subject to the vagaries of the seasons. The summers of 1983 and '84 were good by recent standards, that of 1985 one of the worst on record, but it was followed by an exceptionally fine autumn. A succession of three poor springs has probably meant that single brooded, early species are "under-recorded", and a few remaining colonies of the Grizzled Skipper could have been completely overlooked.

All the records will be fed into the data bank of the Suffolk Biological Records Centre, at the Ipswich Museum. It is hoped that naturalists will continue to forward their records, and so enable Suffolk's butterfly species to be monitored. The real value of the records will probably not be apparent until our successors produce their *"Butterflies of Suffolk"*, perhaps early in the next century, and the two distributions are compared.

Figure 5.
Coverage achieved by the Suffolk Butterfly Survey (1983-85).

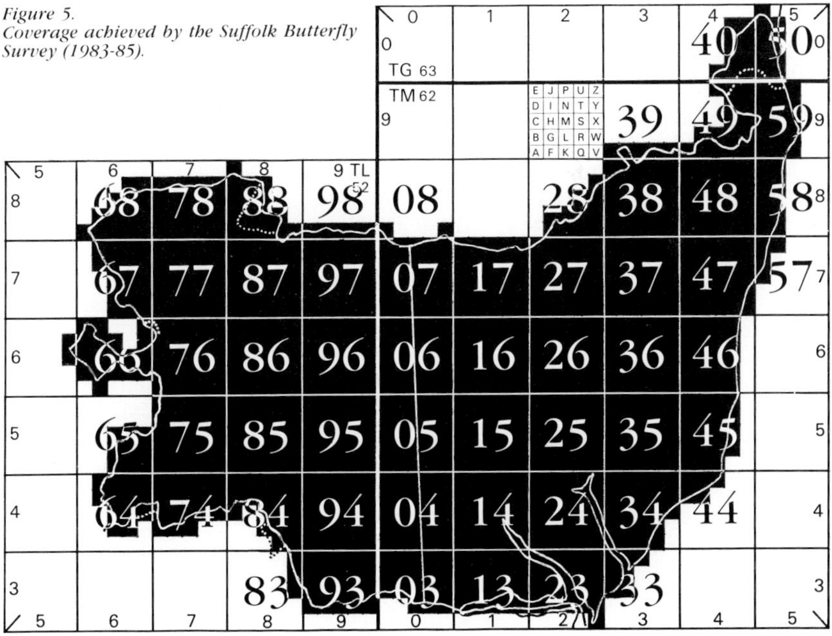

THE CATALOGUE

A LL BUT SEVEN of the British resident species and naturally occurring migrants have at one time or another been found in or claimed for Suffolk. Because of this all species on the British List (Bradley and Fletcher, 1979), less those of doubtful status not recorded from Suffolk, are included in the Catalogue. Those that have never been seriously claimed are listed without comment and marked with an asterisk*. With the exception of the Berger's Clouded Yellow, it is most unlikely that any of these will ever be seen in Suffolk. It will be noticed that in addition to species listed with an asterisk, others said to have occurred in Suffolk have been found to have no justifiable place on the County List.

The Text
There are many excellent guides to the identification and distribution of British butterflies, so only an outline of the important characters by which a species may be separated from similar ones has been given. Greater emphasis is placed on the assessment of past and present distribution and status in Suffolk, in the context of the British distribution. Habitat preferences and flight periods are those for Suffolk, as are the larval food-plants, where known.

Our comments and inferences appear in square brackets [], as do the names of colleagues who have allowed us to use their unpublished observations. Colloquial and scientific food-plant names are those used by Simpson (1982).

The Maps
The area adopted for the Survey and appearing on the distribution maps comprises the Watsonian vice-counties, East Suffolk (25) and West Suffolk (26), except that a small area of mud on the Stour Estuary off Mistley has been ignored. The two vice-counties, divided by the oblique line following the 1°E line of longitude, include two sizeable areas that are now in the administrative county of Norfolk — between Fritton Decoy and Breydon Water to the north of Lowestoft, and south of the River Little Ouse to the west of Thetford — and there are other small but important differences (Mendel, 1984). These are marked on the maps as a dotted line, whereas the vice-county boundary is solid. Together the two vice-counties correspond very closely with the pre-1974 area of Suffolk.

Records are plotted by tetrads (blocks of four 1 km squares, which are the smallest units on the 1:50,000 Ordnance Survey maps), and each of these may be identified by using the alphabetical code letter after the 10 km square reference. Ipswich for example is at TM14. The south-eastern corner of that 10 km square is TM14V.
The following four date classes are used:-

        ✱ 19th century
        ○ 1900-1959
        ● 1960-1979
        ■ 1980-1985

Where a species is so rare that it has only been recorded on a very few occasions, and the majority of records are historical, no map is given. At the other end of the spectrum only records in the most recent date class have been plotted on the distribution maps for the commoner species. These are:-

Small Skipper	Orange Tip	Comma
Essex Skipper	Small Copper	Speckled Wood
Large Skipper	Common Blue	Wall
Clouded Yellow	Holly Blue	Grayling
Brimstone	Red Admiral	Gatekeeper
Large White	Painted Lady	Meadow Brown
Small White	Small Tortoiseshell	Small Heath
Green-veined White	Peacock	Ringlet

On the rest of the maps all the known records have been plotted where they are sufficiently localised. Many have had to be assigned to a particular tetrad and could just as accurately have been assigned to an adjacent one. It was considered more important to include these records which help to show the historical distributions, than omit them altogether. Where records from two date classes coincide, only the most recent has been plotted. This clearly shows contractions of range, but effectively conceals expansions, and for this reason there was no point in plotting the historical records for the Comma. Only records from within the vice-counties have been plotted for tetrads straddling the border.

Although it may be said that total coverage was achieved in the Butterfly Survey (Fig. 5) in that we have one or more records from every tetrad, individual species coverage is not so complete. The commoner species, the Small White, Small Tortoiseshell, Peacock, Gatekeeper, Meadow Brown and probably others are undoubtedly found in every tetrad, and the maps for these species indicate those areas of the County least well surveyed.

An element of observer bias shows on some of the maps, and is perhaps most noticeable in those for the Red Admiral and Painted Lady, two migrants with centres of distribution seemingly coinciding with Ipswich. Some species are better surveyed than others. Single brooded species with a relatively short flying season, such as the Orange Tip and Ringlet, will be missed unless a tetrad is visited at the appropriate season. Species which can survive in small discrete colonies, "skippers" which are small and fly too fast for the untrained eye to notice, and "hairstreaks" in the tree-tops, are all likely to have been overlooked by less expert recorders. Historical records provide only the merest framework of a distribution for all but the rarer species. Unfortunately, few of our predecessors bothered to list localities for then common species such as the Grizzled Skipper. Maps of immigrant species, and to a lesser extent resident species where individual butterflies are highly mobile and wide ranging, do not show "distributions" in the normal sense of the word. Such species have a good chance of turning up anywhere, often miles from likely breeding areas, and the maps need careful interpretation. In spite of these limitations, and the inevitable small percentage of plotting errors, the maps show true and meaningful distributions.

CHEQUERED SKIPPER *Carterocephalus palaemon* Pallas

This attractive little butterfly became extinct in England in the mid-1970's, but still occurs in north-west Scotland, where it was not discovered until 1942.

Stainton (1857) recorded the species from Stowmarket, Suffolk, and this locality has been referred to many times since, even though the record was withdrawn, having *"occurred either from inadvertence, or in consequence of relying too much upon doubtful authorities"* (Greene, 1857). There are no authentic records of the Chequered Skipper from Suffolk.

SMALL SKIPPER *Thymelicus sylvestris* Poda

This butterfly is liable to be confused with the Essex Skipper, unless caught for close inspection. A "glass" bottomed pill box is ideal for this purpose, allowing the diagnostic colour of the under-sides of the antennae to be carefully inspected without harm to the butterfly. For a description of the characters which may be used to separate the two species, see Essex Skipper (p. 32).

The Small Skipper is widely distributed and generally common in Britain as far north as Lancashire and Yorkshire, but is not found in Ireland. In Suffolk it is found wherever there is suitable habitat, though it tends to be less common and more local on the boulder clay and fen areas. It is frequently found in company with the Essex Skipper, though the relative abundance of each species varies in different parts of the County. In the south-east the Essex Skipper is much more numerous, but is replaced completely by the Small Skipper in the north-east. In the north-west, on the fen soils, the Essex almost replaces the Small Skipper. Its status in Suffolk does not seem to have changed over the years, in spite of major changes in the pattern of agriculture. C. R. Bree quickly dismissed the species as *"Common"* (Greene, 1857), as did Bloomfield (1890), though both are likely to have included an unknown proportion of Essex Skippers in their assessment. According to Morley (1937a) it was *"locally abundant in rough-grassy places, from Bures to Bradwell"*, i.e. one end of the County to the other.

Both Small and Essex Skippers thrive on the same habitat and are found wherever the wild grasses on which the larvae feed are allowed to grow to maturity. Field and woodland edges, heathland, coastal cliffs, roadside verges, and even derelict land in urban areas support colonies of both, or either species. The larvae of the Small Skipper will feed on a range of grasses, though in the wild seem to prefer Yorkshire Fog, *Holcus lanatus* L. The larvae on hatching in August are said to spin a cocoon, in which to pass the winter, without feeding.

The single brood of the Small Skipper is on the wing at the end of June or beginning of July, depending on the season, usually a full week before the first Essex Skippers are seen. Worn specimens may still be found in early September if the weather is favourable.

Small Skipper ♂ (lower), Essex Skipper ♀ (upper)   *(A. Beaumont)*

Small Skipper

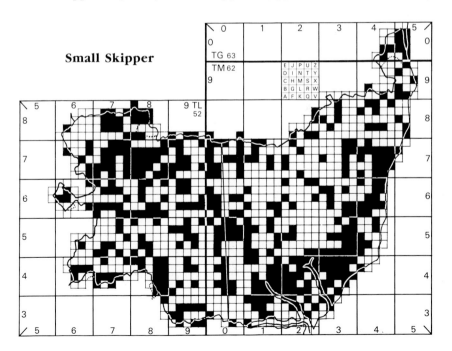

ESSEX SKIPPER   *Thymelicus lineola* Ochs.

The Essex and Small Skippers are very likely to be confused, being of the same fulvous colour, about the same size, and occurring in the same type of habitat. The two species are most reliably separated by the colour of the under-side of the tips of their antennae. In the Essex Skipper this is black (but with a slight rufous tinge in females), whilst in the Small Skipper it ranges from light orange to brown. Small Skippers with dark upper-sides to their antennae and brown under-tips may cause confusion, as may late season female Essex Skippers when the rufous tint to the antennal tips becomes more pronounced. The former have been found more frequently towards the north-east of their range in the County. Another useful character in the male Essex Skipper is the shorter, much less distinct, and less oblique sexual mark of the fore wing.

The Essex Skipper was the last of the resident British species to be discovered, and only recognised as distinct from the Small Skipper in 1889. For many years it was considered to be a species more or less restricted to the coastal areas of Essex and North Kent, and even though confusion with the Small Skipper has resulted in its being "under-recorded" in the past, there is no doubt that in the last 40 years it has both extended its range in Suffolk and become considerably more common. In the 1930's and 40's there was in Suffolk an energetic band of competent collectors, well able to recognise the species, yet Vinter (1943) quoting P. J. Burton writes *"One of several Skippers I took home from Bentley Woods on 25 July I find to be* Lineola *from this new and Suffolk's most northern locality, though it is a score of miles south of Wicken Fen to which the species is known to extend in Cambs"*. Bentley Woods is less than 5 miles from the Essex border, and by that time the species had also been recorded from Bures, Felixstowe and Bawdsey (Morley, 1937a). Even then Morley considered that it was probably, *"a good deal wider distributed to the north [of the Essex/Suffolk border] than has yet been ascertained"*. This was known to be the case when Burton (1944) found the species at Monk Soham, but it is clear that in those days the Essex Skipper was considered a scarce and very local south Suffolk butterfly.

It is now found throughout Suffolk excepting the extreme north-east, and the map opposite is probably a true picture of its distribution. In the south of the County and the Breck it is very much more numerous than the Small Skipper, and the two frequently fly together. The Essex Skipper is a species of rank, dry grassland and even quite small areas such as roadside verges may support large colonies. It is particularly plentiful in cuttings and on embankments of the new A45, and road systems and railways may well have helped its spread.

The larvae are reported to feed on a variety of grass species, but especially Cocksfoot, *Dactylis glomerata* L. and Creeping Soft-grass, *Holcus mollis* L. (Heath, Pollard and Thomas, 1984). The eggs, unlike those of the Small Skipper, do not hatch until the following spring.

* LULWORTH SKIPPER   *Thymelicus acteon* Rott.

Essex Skipper   *(A.C. Hubbard)*

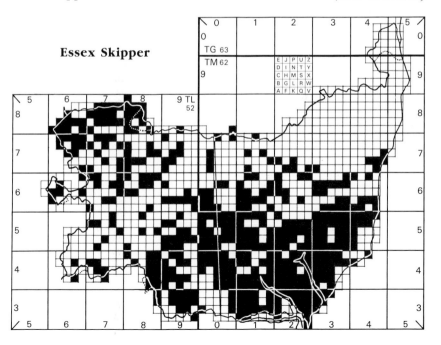

Essex Skipper

SILVER-SPOTTED SKIPPER   *Hesperia comma* L.

A very local and declining butterfly of calcareous grassland in southern Britain, the Silver-spotted Skipper has not been seen in Suffolk for a century.

It was *"discovered in considerable abundance towards the middle of August 1825 on the Devil's Ditch"* (Stephens, 1827-8), Cambridgeshire, and subsequently recorded from the adjacent Newmarket Heath (Newman, 1871-2) which straddles the Suffolk/Cambridgeshire border. According to Morley (1937a) its presence on Newmarket Heath, Suffolk, in about 1880 was confirmed by M. M., T. and B. Brown.

LARGE SKIPPER   *Ochlodes venata* Brem. & Grey

Only marginally larger than the Small and Essex Skippers, and showing a similar bright orange-brown upperside, the Large Skipper may be known by the distinctive mottling of its wings. This is evident on both the upper and under-sides, and is most pronounced in the females. The tips of the antennae are black, but, unlike those of the Essex Skipper, distinctly hooked.

A common species throughout Britain as far north as southern Scotland, the Large Skipper is as plentiful in Suffolk today as the records show it has always been. It is found throughout the County wherever the grasses are allowed to grow tall, but prefers damper, more sheltered localities than the Small or Essex Skippers. Woodland rides, glades and borders, damp meadows, riversides and country lanes, all provide suitable habitat, and Large Skippers may be numerous in the more open areas of conifer plantations. Like most of the skippers, they will sit in a characteristic manner with the fore wings slightly apart above the back, and hind wings open wide at right angles. Favourite perches are the leaves of Bramble or Bracken in sunny spots, but for much of the time this active little butterfly will move restlessly from one leaf or blade of grass to another.

Although in exceptional seasons the Large Skipper may be on the wing at the end of May, it is seldom seen in Suffolk until the middle of June. There is one generation of butterflies a year, and this has usually finished by mid-August. However, a colony of freshly emerged specimens at Lakenheath on 27th August 1984, several weeks after the species had finished over the rest of the County, suggests a partial second brood. The possibility of the Large Skipper being double brooded in Britain has been argued by lepidopterists for many years.

The eggs are laid on the blades of various grasses, but the principal larval foodplant is thought to be Cock's-foot, *Dactylis glomerata* L., a very common species in Suffolk. The larvae will also feed on the almost equally common Wood False Brome, *Brachypodium sylvaticum* (Huds.) Beauv.

Large Skipper +   *(A. Beaumont)*

Large Skipper

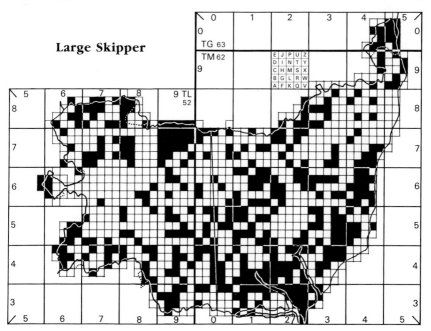

DINGY SKIPPER   *Erynnis tages* L.

A small grey-brown moth-like butterfly, the Dingy Skipper is very appropriately named. The males may easily be known by the distinctive fold along the basal half of the front margin of the fore wings, and in addition the ground colour of the upper surface tends to be darker and less contrasting. Though unlikely to be mistaken for any other British butterfly, it may be confused with certain day-flying moths. Both Mother Shipton, *Callistege mi* Cl. and Common Heath, *Ematurga atomaria* L. look superficially very similar, and in Suffolk are found in the same habitat at the same time of the year.

The Dingy Skipper was always regarded as "locally common" in Suffolk, and throughout much of its British range, though it was scarcer in the north of England and in Scotland. Greene (1857) wrote that it was *"Common, but local"* in Suffolk and Bloomfield (1890), *"Locally common"*. Morley (1937a), less than fifty years ago, found it to be more local than the Grizzled Skipper, *"pretty well confined to open spaces within and upon the skirts of woods, throughout nearly the whole County"*. Since then populations have crashed, though not as dramatically as those of the Grizzled Skipper. Because the Dingy Skipper was considered common, and is less attractive and noticeable than most species, it was not systematically recorded and the period of decline is difficult to pinpoint. It seems, however, to have become much scarcer as early as the late 1950's. Today the stronghold of the Dingy Skipper in Suffolk is the King's Forest, where it is still plentiful along the well managed rides between stands of conifers. Outside this area colonies are small and it must be considered a rarity. This species was not recorded from East Suffolk during the Survey years.

The Dingy Skipper is a grassland butterfly found in a wide variety of habitat types including woodland rides, chalk pits, heathland and railway cuttings. The common factor is a plentiful supply of the larval foodplant, Bird's-foot Trefoil, *Lotus corniculatus* L. This plant is found most frequently on the lighter, poorer soils, especially in areas fairly well grazed by rabbits. The decline of the Dingy Skipper is difficult to explain. The Common Blue, which also depends on the same foodplant, is fairly common throughout Suffolk. Perhaps the Dingy Skipper's poor mobility and liking for sunny, sheltered sites are important factors.

In early springs the Dingy Skipper may be on the wing in late April, but mid-May is more usual in Suffolk. A few worn individuals are often still about in early July, and very occasionally there is a partial second brood in August. The Dingy Skipper's rapid zig-zag flight makes it difficult to see until it settles, wings spread, on a low flower or bare patch of earth. This behaviour, combined with the moth-like appearance, and the formation of small, discrete colonies, makes it likely that new sites will be discovered. There is no doubt, however, that the species has declined drastically over the last twenty-five years.

Dingy Skipper *(J. O'Sullivan)*

Dingy Skipper

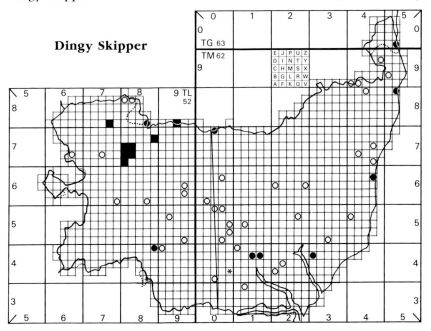

GRIZZLED SKIPPER *Pyrgus malvae* L.

This attractive little butterfly with "black and white" chequered wings is unlikely to be confused with any other as it darts from one sunny perch to another in late spring. It flies very quickly when disturbed and is virtually invisible on the wing, unlike the Common Heath, *Ematurga atomaria* L. and the Latticed Heath, *Semiothisa clathrata* (L.), two day-flying moths which may be mistaken for it by the uninitiated.

The Grizzled Skipper is found widely across central and southern England and in Wales and, according to Heath, Pollard and Thomas (1984), although its range *"has not changed greatly"* except for some contraction in the extreme north, *"it has become an uncommon species"* in the east of England. This is something of an understatement so far as Suffolk is concerned. There was not a single confirmed record during the course of the Survey, and there is every likelihood that the Grizzled Skipper has virtually disappeared from the County. It was last recorded on 19th May 1979 at Felshamhall Wood, though probably still exists in small numbers in a few localities. The species is single brooded, only on the wing for a few weeks in late spring when the weather is often poor, flies rapidly, and may form small, discrete colonies. It is therefore easily overlooked when reduced to low numbers.

The status of the Grizzled Skipper in Suffolk in the 19th century is well summarised by Greene (1857), *"Common, but local"*, and Bloomfield (1890), *"Somewhat common"*. The status remained unchanged when Morley (1937a) wrote *"Nowadays, there can be no doubt that every extensive piece of waste pasture possess its Grizzled Skippers in the spring"*, except that it was *"rare in the north-east"* of the County. The species was found in a variety of habitats: grazing marshes and fen, brick pits, railway embankments and open areas associated with woodlands. Rough pastures on woodland edges were especially favoured, but this habitat has now almost gone, replaced by cereal and beet-fields. It is difficult to determine the onset of the decline, because few entomologists systematically recorded such common species! Certainly it was becoming scarce by the late 1960's, but the decline may have started earlier.

The larvae feed on Wild Strawberry, *Fragaria vesca* L., Barren Strawberry, *Potentilla sterilis* (L.) Garcke and Bramble, *Rubus* spp., though we only know of one instance of a larva found in Suffolk. Mrs. E. M. Beaufoy found one in a curled-over leaf of Wild Strawberry growing on a railway embankment at Bentley in the 1940's [S. Beaufoy].

In early seasons the Grizzled Skipper may be on the wing in April and, when conditions are favourable, some may still be found into July. A partial second brood is exceptional and has not been recorded in Suffolk.

Grizzled Skipper   *(B. Sawford)*

Grizzled Skipper

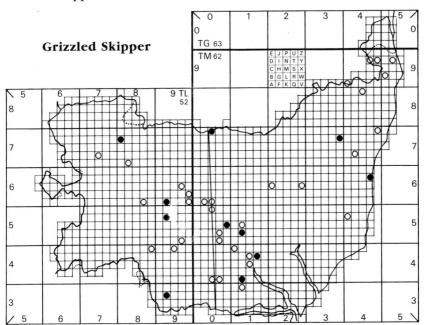

APOLLO *Parnassius apollo* L.

A continental species, sometimes known as the Crimson Ringed Butterfly, which is widely distributed in mountainous regions of Western Europe, including southern Scandinavia.

The Apollo has from time to time been found in Britain, and Morley and Chalmers-Hunt (1959), who list the records to that date, consider that at least some may have been true migrants. The single Suffolk record relates to a specimen netted but not taken on *"the coast at Thorpe by Aldeburgh on 10 September, 1928"* (Vinter, 1929), by a Mrs. Webb.

Larvae of the Apollo feed on Stonecrop, *Sedum* and Houseleek, *Sempervivum*, and pupate in a loose cocoon spun amongst the food-plant near the ground, *"so that it might easily be imported with horticultural specimens for the rock garden or alpine house which might account for some of the records"* (Howarth, 1973).

SWALLOWTAIL *Papilio machaon* L.

The British Swallowtail (subspecies *britannicus* Seitz) is a wetland butterfly now confined to the Norfolk Broads, though in the last century it was found more widely across the fenland of East Anglia, and perhaps also on the Thames marshes. The Continental form (ssp. *bigeneratus* Ver.), which is less heavily marked with black is strictly double rather than usually single brooded, and found in a range of habitats. There is evidence that this Continental subspecies, which is now an occasional migrant, was resident in southern England until the early part of the 19th century (Bretherton, 1951b) and was lost as a result of our deteriorating climate.

From records alone it is impossible to separate the British and Continental subspecies, and even preserved specimens can sometimes be difficult to assign, as distinguishing characters overlap. The situation in Suffolk is further confused by the considerable number of attempted introductions and deliberate releases.

There is surprisingly little evidence to suggest that the British Swallowtail was ever a breeding species in Suffolk, in spite of a common border with both Cambridgeshire (a former stronghold) and Norfolk. It is, however, very likely that the species was once found regularly on the fens along the River Lark near Tuddenham. T. and J. Brown knew of the insect in this area, *"Between Tuddenham and Mildenhall"* (Bloomfield, 1890), and Morley (1937a) dates the record to about 1880. E. J. G. Sparke told Morley that in 1901 *"a young friend of mine saw two in Tuddenham Fen and I caught one, but let it go again. . .they once flew all along the stream to Mildenhall, according to old accounts"* (Morley, 1933a).

There are many other records scattered across the County, and it is very difficult to decide whether they are migrants, releases, introductions or the progeny of such, or stray individuals from localities

Swallowtail   *(J. O'Sullivan)*

in Norfolk or Cambridgeshire. Some of the deliberate introductions have
been documented:-

> *"Fritton, where a few Swallow-tail* (Papilio machaon) *larvae
> have been put down upon the abundant* Peucedanum palustre
> *this year. . ."*

(Anon, 1936)

> *". . . our Member Hugh Buxton began bringing small plants
> of* Peucedanum palustre, *Moen., from Catfield and installing
> them round his small pond at Snape a decade ago. They
> increased well and he used to scatter the seed on to the
> adjacent marshes. During 1937-8 he brought* Machaon
> caterpillars from the same Norfolk marsh. . ."*

(Waterfield, 1944)

> *"A few which emerged from pupae collected in Norfolk, were
> liberated at Herringfleet. (P. J.) I released twelve there from
> pupae obtained from same source (H.E.J.) July."*

(Anon, 1948)

The larvae of our native Swallowtail feed almost exclusively on Milk
Parsley (Hog's Fennel), *Peucedanum palustre* (L.) Moench, whilst
migrants are less particular and will use a variety of umbellifers including
Angelica, *Angelica sylvestris* L., Fennel, *Foeniculum vulgare* Mill., Wild
and cultivated Carrot, *Daucus carota* L. Larvae of migrant origin have

been recorded from Suffolk, for example ". . . *on 18 September last (by Miss Long, I believe) feeding on ordinary cultivated Carrot in a Pakefield garden*" (Goddard, 1943), in 1945 on "*Snape garden Fennel*" (Anon, 1945b) and "*One larva, feeding on carrot, was found in Wenhaston, during Sept.*" (Anon, 1947a).

Suffolk records are far too numerous to list, and to plot them on a map would be meaningless because of their mixed origin. The most exceptional year was 1945 when over two dozen were recorded between 15th July and 11th August, and according to Morley (1945a) "*That none, or but a negligible proportion of the specimens, were indigenous (Snape, Lowestoft), seems sufficiently proved by the utter absence of any first brood here*", but always there must be a little doubt when poorly documented releases are taking place. It is interesting that "*of nineteen records, mainly of the continental subspecies*" in Dorset since the early part of the 19th century, ten were in 1945 (Thomas and Webb, 1984), adding weight to the argument that this was an exceptional year for Swallowtail migration.

WOOD WHITE *Leptidea sinapis* L.

During the 19th century the Wood White could be found locally over much of England and Wales, but by the early 1900's had disappeared from most of its northern localities, and had become much scarcer towards the east of its range. Today the species appears to have strongholds in only four areas of England: "*Herefordshire and Worcestershire; Northamptonshire and Oxfordshire; the borders of Surrey and Sussex; and east Devon and South Somerset*" (Warren, 1984). It is still widespread in Ireland and seems to have been expanding its range in England in recent years.

There are 19th century Suffolk records for: Raydon Wood in 1850 and 1851 "*where I have been told, the late Mr John Hoy once took the larvae abundantly*" (Postans, 1858); "*a wood near Stowmarket*" (Greene, 1857); "*Brandeston and Playford* — Joseph Greene; *Stowmarket and Bentley* — H. H. Crewe" (Newman, 1870-71); Needham "*but not within the last thirty years*" and "*Wherstead about ten years ago, Mr. H. Haward*" (Bloomfield, 1890). Bloomfield considered the Wood White to be "*almost extinct*" in Suffolk by that time, but another was taken "*at Yarmouth south of Breydon in 1890 (Nat. Gazette iii, 13)*" (Morley, 1937a). It is clear from the records that the species had always been very scarce in Suffolk.

Nothing more is known except one "*flapped quite slowly and gently with its characteristic flight past, within a yard of me, as I was strolling within the edge of a wood a mile or so from Halesworth, at noon 19 May last*" (Morley, 1932a).

PALE CLOUDED YELLOW   *Colias hyale* L.
*BERGER'S CLOUDED YELLOW   *Colias australis* Ver.

These two very scarce migrant species are so similar that it was not until 1947 that they were recognised as distinct. Records are further confused by the pale form of the female Clouded Yellow (f. *helice* Hübner), which is more common than either.

There are no definite records of Berger's Clouded Yellow from Suffolk, but the Pale Clouded Yellow has occurred regularly. Morley (1937a) lists the Suffolk records from 1811 and remarks, "*this species occurs usually along with the last one [Clouded Yellow] and is of rather more than double its rarity.*"

Since that time it has only been seen as follows: **1938** — "*one only in a field of lucerne at Whitton 29 Aug. (Miss King)*" (Morley, 1938); **1943** — one at Walsham-le-Willows (Davey, 1943); **1945** — singly at Aldringham, 17th July (D. G. Garnett), Waldringfield, 17th Sept. (A. P. Waller) and Frostenden, 1st. Oct. (Anon, 1945b); **1947** — September, eight "*at Stowmarket by 12th (Aston)*" (Morley, 1947b) and others later in the same lucerne field; "*I caught in my hands a single. . . at Sizewell on 14 September. . .D. G. Garnett*", and "*Member Peacock tells me he saw a single. . .at Parham on 17 Sept.*" (Morley, 1947c); at least four at Bosmere, 27/28 Sept., J. Burton and 1st Oct., E. W. Platten (H. E. Chipperfield Coll., Ipswich Museum); one "*at Ousden. . . on October 8 (D. W. H. Ffennell)*" (Riley, 1947); and at Benacre, C. G. M. de Worms (Beaufoy, 1970); **1948** — "*On June 15 my wife saw six. . . on the shingle just south of Aldeburgh and another on June 16 between Aldeburgh and Thorpeness*" (Blackie, 1948), **1949** — "*A single at Wingfield College on 3 October. D. C. Edwards*" (Morley, 1949).

There have been no reports since 1949 and the Pale Clouded Yellow must now be regarded as very much rarer than the Clouded Yellow.

Both the Pale and Berger's Clouded Yellow are known to breed in this country in favourable years, and it is likely that concentrations as found by A. E. Aston in a lucerne field at Stowmarket in 1947 are a result of local breeding. The larvae of the Pale Clouded Yellow feed on Lucerne, *Medicago sativa* L. or Clover, *Trifolium* spp., whilst those of Berger's Clouded Yellow feed on Horseshoe Vetch, *Hippocrepis comosa* L. or the introduced Crown Vetch, *Coronilla varia* L. "Pale" Clouded Yellows from chalk areas of West Suffolk, where the Horseshoe Vetch grows, should be carefully examined in the hope that they might be Berger's.

CLOUDED YELLOW   *Colias croceus* Geoffr.

This is one of the more regular of the scarce migrant species, appearing in small numbers most years. The males and normal females are easily recognised by their bright orange-yellow colour, but the pale form of the female (f. *helice* Hübner) is likely to be confused with the previous species.

In spite of the yellowish-white ground colour the "*helice*" females may be known by the heavy black borders to their wings, especially the hind wings, which are only lightly marked in both Pale and Berger's Clouded Yellows. However, this distinguishing character may be difficult to see in the field because "clouded yellows" close their wings tightly immediately they settle.

Occasionally large numbers of Clouded Yellows reach our shores, but such "Clouded Yellow years" are exceptional. Morley (1937a) summarises the species' occurrence in Suffolk to that date:-

"... *it has been periodical and generally rare, with certain years of peculiar influx, such as the above 1826, 1856 when it abounded on our coast (Ent. Wk. Int. v, 30), 1858 when Joseph Gedge took ten near Bury (l.c.iv, 187), 1892 when it appeared in profusion far inland and (EMM. xxviii, 287) abounded round Southwold, 1900 when it was sporadic only (EMM. 1900, 238), 1906 when it was sparse (Ent. 1906, 234), 1917 when a few penetrated to Darmsden and Baylham (l.c. 1917, 259), 1921 when it occurred at Saxstead, etc. (Vinter), with a small immigration during 1922 and much larger one in 1928*".

This list is by no means complete, but even so it is somewhat surprising that there is no mention of the "Great Clouded Yellow Year" of 1877, an exceptional year for the species in Britain as a whole.

Records show that the Clouded Yellow was more common in the late 1930's and 40's, and years of particular plenty were 1938, 1941, 1946 and especially 1947. It appeared regularly but by no means every year in the 1950's and 60's, but the 1970's and 80's were lean years, except for 1983. This was undoubtedly a "Clouded Yellow year." Butterflies were seen during the second week of June and there were reports until the end of October. They were most plentiful towards the end of July and in August, and there is little doubt that freshly emerged specimens at this time were the progeny of early arrivals, though these may have been supplemented by a second wave of migrants (Bretherton and Chalmers-Hunt, 1985). Fresh specimens at the end of September suggested a second brood in some areas of Suffolk. Numbers of "*helice*" females were seen, but, surprisingly, in contrast with 1947 not a single Pale Clouded Yellow was identified with certainty.

The Clouded Yellow is a Mediterranean species, which produces a succession of generations throughout the year and has no dormant stage able to survive our winters. It has been known to arrive in Britain as early as April (Howarth, 1973) but late May or June is more usual. The larvae feed on Clover, *Trifolium* spp., Lucerne, *Medicago sativa* L. and other leguminous plants, and the number of butterflies seen in August depends on local breeding success. Clover and Lucerne are now grown less commonly as fodder crops, and so perhaps the Clouded Yellow will never again be as common as it was in 1947. Later in the season there is evidence of a return migration, though this has not been noted in Suffolk.

Clouded Yellow (f. *helice* Hübner)   *(H. Mendel)*

Clouded Yellow
(1983 records only)

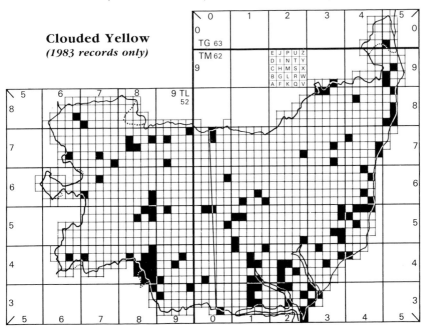

BRIMSTONE *Gonepteryx rhamni* L.

The unusual angular wing shape will readily separate the Brimstone from all other British species. The bright sulphur-yellow males and pale yellow-green females are most conspicuous in early spring, and easily recognised on the wing. However, later in the season, the females are often passed over for Large Whites which have a very similar flight action.

The Brimstone has been recorded from nearly every county in England and Wales, though it is far more local in the north. Its distribution and status in Suffolk have changed little since Bloomfield (1890) wrote that it was "*Common*". There has probably been some decrease in numbers since that time, but Morley's "*hardly a common butterfly (cf. Trans. ii, 182) and rarest with us in High Suffolk*" (Morley, 1937a) is somewhat surprising. Today the Brimstone is found throughout Suffolk, but there is a strong western bias in the distribution, no doubt related to the distribution of the larval foodplants, Buckthorn, *Rhamnus catharticus* L. and Alder Buckthorn, *Frangula alnus* Mill. According to Simpson (1982), the former, though frequent in parts of West Suffolk, is "*Rare or almost extinct in East Suffolk*". Alder Buckthorn is scarce in the County and again more frequent in the west.

In view of the known distribution of the larval foodplants it is surprising how frequently the Brimstone is seen in East Suffolk. It is, however, a strong flyer and will often wander far from the breeding areas. Pollard and Hall (1980) have suggested that it is "*possible that individuals which leave a breeding area to overwinter return to the same site*", but a general dispersal seems more likely.

The single generation of adults is on the wing from late July and may be seen on fine days until the end of September or later. The butterflies seek out the nectar flowers of waysides and woodland edges, and are particularly attracted to Knapweeds. From September they take up their winter quarters amongst Brambles, Holly, Ivy or some other evergreen. Their wing shape and colour make them virtually invisible, especially when hanging amongst the leaves of Ivy. Brimstones will not be seen again until awakened by the sunny days of March or April and, on emergence from hibernation, are often in such remarkably good condition that it was once thought that there were two generations each year. The Brimstone is the longest lived of all the British species, and butterflies from the previous year may sometimes be seen in July in company with those that are freshly emerged.

CLEOPATRA *Gonepteryx cleopatra* L.

A south European species resembling the Brimstone, and most unlikely to reach these shores of its own accord. The few examples reputed to have been taken in Britain, if genuine, have probably been accidentally or deliberately introduced.

Of the four male specimens at the British Museum (Natural History) taken in Britain, one is labelled from Aldeburgh, 1896 (Howarth, 1973).

Brimstone   *(R. Beecroft)*

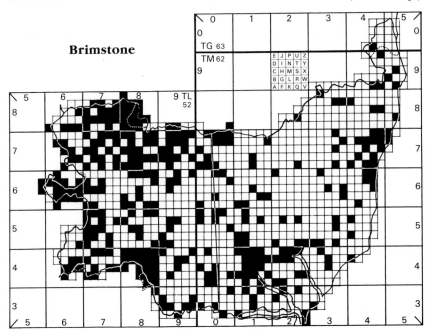

Brimstone

BLACK-VEINED WHITE *Aporia crataegi* L.

Though once locally abundant over a wide area of England and Wales, the Black-veined White declined dramatically from the middle of the last century, and became extinct in Britain in the 1920's.

The single Suffolk record dates back to Curtis (1831), and was rather prematurely dismissed by Bloomfield (1890) as, *"Very probably a mistake"*. Dale (1887) accepted Curtis' record, and later adds that in Suffolk it *"has long been an extinct species"* (Dale, 1890). According to Morley (1937a); *"John Curtis is entirely reliable, and upon his word we may well depend for the species' erstwhile occurrence in our County"*. Morley also refers to an *"ancient example, reputed local. . . yet existing in the collection of the late Dr. Donald Hutchinson of Lowestoft"*, but gives little weight to this as evidence of the species' occurrence in Suffolk.

In view of the Black-veined White's once wide distribution, there would appear to be no definite reason to doubt the authenticity of Curtis' Suffolk record.

LARGE WHITE *Pieris brassicae* L.

The largest of the three common "whites" generally lumped together as "cabbage whites" and, with the Small White, one of the very few British species known to cause crop damage. The third member of the trio, the Green-veined White, only lays its eggs on wild members of the Cabbage family (Cruciferae) and is not a pest.

The Large White is an attractive butterfly, white on the upper surface except for the broadly black wing tips and a small spot on the front margin of the hind wing in the males, and with two additional spots and a mark along the hind margin of the fore wing in the females. In the spring brood these markings are grey rather than black and less distinct. The Large White has always been common and widespread in Suffolk, but the numbers can fluctuate greatly from year to year, as happened in the Survey years. There were plenty of Large Whites to be seen throughout 1983 and 85, but the first brood in 1984 was almost non-existent. Indeed, the first specimen seen by us was in late June, flying low over the shingle on the seaward side of Orford Ness, and heading north. This species is a well known migrant and this, in part, determines seasonal abundance in Britain. It is interesting that 1984 was a poor year for other spring migrants such as the Red Admiral and Painted Lady, and the Large White was scarce until late July.

Several mass immigrations have been recorded in Suffolk. In July 1943, G. Baker reported *"that at Southwold cliff a continuous flock with less than a yard between the individual* Pieris brassicae, *L., came in from the east between 8.30 and 10 am on 28th, as well as between 8 and 9.30 am on 29th; and that upon both days, they were observed going westward by longshore fishermen two miles from the coast"* (Anon, 1943). Similar events were witnessed in 1945 (Anon, 1945a) and in 1958 (Anon, 1958b) and are no doubt of regular occurrence.

Large White ♀   *(A. Beaumont)*

Large White

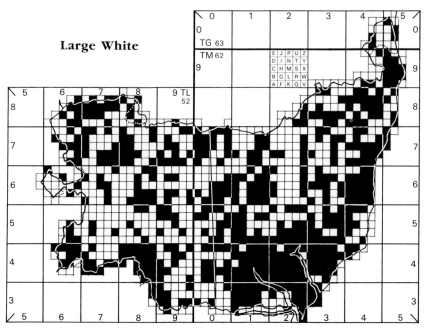

The eggs are laid in batches on the underside of the leaves of the larval food plant, normally various types of cultivated Cabbage, *Brassica* spp., including Brussels Sprouts, Kale and Broccoli, or the garden Nasturtium, *Tropaeolum majus* L. Larvae are also known to feed on Wild Mignonette, *Reseda lutea* L. (Brooks and Knight, 1982), and in Suffolk have been seen to feed on the related Dyer's Rocket (Weld), *Reseda luteola* L. They are particularly susceptible to the ravages of parasitic wasps, and one in particular, *Apanteles glomeratus* L., can be very destructive, and is thought to be one of the causes of population fluctuations.

There are two generations of Large White each year, and sometimes a partial third brood. Butterflies may be seen on the wing at any time between late April and early October. Although congregations may be seen in the vicinity of cabbage fields, individuals wander relentlessly and would have been found in every part of the County had there been sufficient recorders.

SMALL WHITE   *Pieris rapae*   L.

Easily confused in the field with both the Large and the Green-veined Whites; this trio without doubt frustrates the recorder. "Whites" are very manoeuvrable on the wing, often wander long distances without settling and, unless netted, identification may at best be tentative. The Small White lacks the well marked veins of the Green-veined White, but except for the smaller size and the single spot near the middle of the fore wing in the male, is marked as the Large White. Again the dark markings of the spring brood are much paler, and may be virtually absent.

The Small White is abundant and widespread in Suffolk, as it is throughout most of Britain, and has been since recording began. It is a very mobile species likely to be found anywhere and everywhere in the County, though concentrations will form where the larval food-plants, usually the various members of the Cabbage family (Cruciferae), are grown. The larvae can be a pest of farm and garden and as well as Cabbages will attack Mignonette, *Reseda odorata* L. and Nasturtium, *Tropaeolum majus* L. Larvae feed on various crucifers in the wild including Hoary Cress, *Cardaria draba* (L.) Desv. (West, 1982), an alien now very common in Suffolk.

There are two, and often three generations each year, and butterflies may be seen throughout the season between late April and early October, except for a short period between the first and second broods. The Small White is nearly always more abundant than the Large White and populations are considerably more stable, though regularly supplemented by immigrants from the Continent.

Small White ♂   *(H. Mendel)*

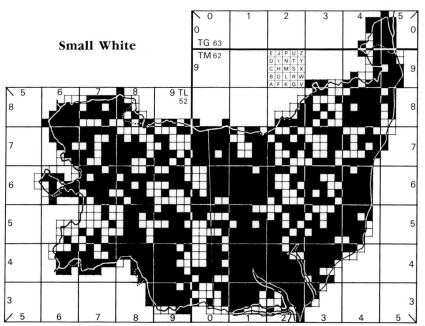

Small White

GREEN-VEINED WHITE   *Pieris napi* L.

It seems extremely likely that, during the Survey, butterflies of this species were frequently overlooked by the "garden recorders", and passed over as Small Whites. The size and markings are in fact very similar, except for the dark scaling along the wing veins in the Green-veined White which is especially pronounced on the under-side of the hind wings. The "green veins" on the upper-side are usually more evident in females, and in common with all the "cabbage whites", the summer generation is more heavily marked.

There are few commoner or more widely distributed species in Britain. In Suffolk the Green-veined White favours damper areas such as woodland edges and riverside meadows, but may be seen anywhere and is a frequent garden visitor. Large numbers are sometimes attracted to fields of crucifers, especially Rape, *Brassica napus* L., but the larvae are not considered a pest and feed mainly on wild species. Known foodplants include Hedge Mustard, *Sisymbrium officinale* (L.) Scop., Garlic Mustard, *Alliaria petiolata* (Bieb.) Cavara & Grande, Horse Radish, *Armoracia rusticana* Gaertn., Mey. & Scherb. and Watercress, *Nasturtium officinale* R. Br.

There are two generations each year and, although butterflies may appear from mid-April onwards, it is usually May before large numbers are seen. The second brood is on the wing from mid-July through to September, and occasionally there is a partial third brood. Unlike the Large and Small Whites, populations of the Green-veined White are not thought to be regularly reinforced by migrants from the Continent.

BATH WHITE   *Pontia daplidice* L.

A migratory species distributed widely across Southern and Central Europe, the Bath White seldom reaches Britain. Though usually seen singly and very rarely, favourable circumstances occasionally coincide to produce a "Bath White year", when comparatively large numbers arrive. Such a year was 1872, when over thirty were captured in Britain, two of them from Suffolk in September; "*by Mr. Wm. Pawsey, at Felixstowe*" (Anon, 1872), and "*Mr. A. E. Garrod at Aldeburgh, on 6th*" (Hunt, 1872).

None were reported from Suffolk in "The Great Bath White Year" of 1945, when many hundreds were recorded, mostly from south-west Britain. However, the following year one was seen and positively identified: "*I observed a butterfly, apparently a large untimely ♀ Orange-tip, sitting upon a plant in meadows just to the south of Needham Market and near the river Gipping on 16 August last; but, after approaching to within ten feet, I quite clearly saw that it was* Pieris daplidice, *Linn.*" (Platten, 1946).

The Bath White which was "*taken on the high road near Newmarket Heath, and was shown to me alive by the captor, Mr. Jobson*" (Brown, 1858), could have been the earliest Suffolk record, but may equally well have been taken over the border in Cambridgeshire.

Green-veined White ♂ *(R. Beecroft)*

Green-veined White

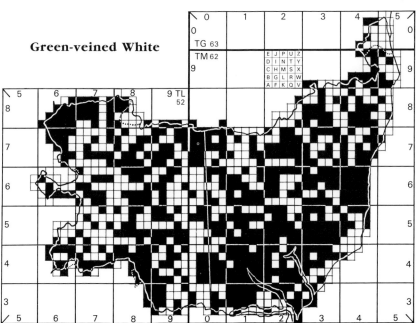

ORANGE TIP *Anthocharis cardamines* L.

The male is aptly named and easily identified, even on the wing, but the female lacks the distinctive orange patch and is all too easily dismissed as a Small or Green-veined White. Both sexes may be known by the most attractive green and white mottled under-side to the hind wings, which shows through giving the upper-side a dappled appearance. At night and during bad weather the fore wings are tucked behind the hind wings making the butterfly very difficult to see, especially when roosting on the flowers of Garlic Mustard, the principal foodplant.

The Orange Tip is found throughout much of Britain, but is considerably more local in the North of England and Scotland. It is widespread and generally common in Suffolk, though more local over the intensive arable areas and near the coast, and no longer an *"abundant species everywhere"* (Morley, 1937a). It is a butterfly of damp pastures, woodland edges, country lanes and hedgerows, especially common in south Suffolk and the fenland of the north-west. A regular visitor to gardens, the Orange Tip is usually seen "passing through", rather than lingering for any length of time.

Although the Orange Tip is probably "under-recorded", due to a succession of wet springs in the Survey years, the eggs are easily found regardless of the weather. They are white when laid, but soon turn bright orange and this, combined with their characteristic bottle shape, makes them easy to find, and provides a very useful means of recording the species. Eggs are laid in the flower heads or on the developing seed pods of various species of the Cabbage family (Cruciferae). A wide range of foodplant species is recognised. In Suffolk Jack-by-the-Hedge (Garlic Mustard), *Alliaria petiolata* (Bieb.) Cavara & Grande is most widely chosen, but towards the end of its flowering season eggs are found more often on Black Mustard, *Brassica nigra* (L.) Koch, which is then in full flower. In the King's Forest area of West Suffolk, Orange Tips lay freely on Field Pepperwort, *Lepidium campestre* (L.) R.Br., but it is perhaps dangerous to assume that eggs are laid only on the most suitable foodplants. Cuckoo Flower (Lady's Smock), *Cardamine pratensis* L., Hedge Mustard, *Sisymbrium officinale* (L.) Scop. and Dame's Violet, *Hesperis matronalis* L., a naturalised garden escape, are other well known larval foodplants.

The larvae feed on the developing seed-pods of the foodplant, and in the later stages are extremely well camouflaged, closely resembling them. They will eat any eggs or small larvae of their own species they come across and "fight" larger ones (George, 1969). It is interesting that larvae of the Green-veined White, which may share the same foodplant, feed on the leaves.

A few Orange Tips are sometimes seen as early as mid-April, but mid-May is more usual, and the single generation is normally over by the beginning of July. Exceptionally, butterflies are seen in August or September, and these are thought to represent a partial second brood, which has not been recorded in Suffolk. Late summer female Orange Tips should always be examined very carefully in case they prove to be specimens of the Bath White, a rare migrant from the Continent.

Orange Tip ♂   *(A. Beaumont)*

Orange Tip

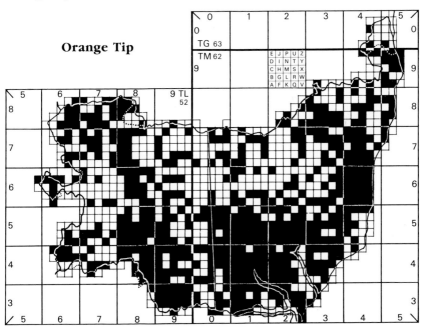

GREEN HAIRSTREAK   *Callophrys rubi* L.

Both sexes of this small butterfly with scalloped hind wings are dark bronze-brown on the upper-side and an unusual iridescent green beneath. The white line, or "hairstreak", across the under-side is usually reduced to a series of spots or streaks, and is most evident on the hind wings.

The Green Hairstreak is generally distributed though local throughout Britain, and is probably the commonest of the hairstreaks. This was true for Suffolk when Bloomfield (1890) wrote that it was "*Generally distributed and not uncommon*" and in the late 1930's it was "*Still generally distributed all over the County*" (Morley, 1937a). Today the Purple Hairstreak is the commoner species in Suffolk, and the Green Hairstreak is more or less confined to heathland. The small colonies once found along woodland edges and in scrubby pastures and railway cuttings across Suffolk have all but gone. However, the species is probably now more common than it was on the Sandlings and Breckland heaths, as a result of the development of huge areas of Gorse, *Ulex* spp. since the introduction of myxomatosis in the 1950's. It is still common on the heaths to the east of Ipswich, and extends well into the town, often venturing into gardens, attracted to flowering shrubs such as Cotoneaster.

A wide variety of larval foodplants is known for the Green Hairstreak, but there is no doubt that in Suffolk, Gorse, *Ulex* spp. and Broom, *Cytisus scoparius* (L.) Link, are most important. In Old Hall Wood, south of Ipswich, butterflies may be found nearly a mile from either of these species, and perhaps Bramble, *Rubus* spp. or Dogwood, *Cornus sanguinea* L., are being used. In Holton Park near Halesworth larvae have been found on Dyer's Greenweed, *Genista tinctoria* L. (Burton, 1941).

The butterflies are on the wing from late April until early July, but are sometimes extremely reluctant to fly. Once disturbed they dart off very quickly, often returning to a favourite perch, and in flight appear dark brown. There is a single generation each year.

BROWN HAIRSTREAK   *Thecla betulae* L.

A late summer butterfly, on the wing in August and September, the Brown Hairstreak frequents woodland and associated thickets and hedgerows where its foodplant Blackthorn, *Prunus spinosa* L. flourishes. It is a secretive species, seldom seen on the wing, and is easily overlooked.

The Brown Hairstreak is a very scarce species in Britain, though colonies have been recorded from many southern, midland and Welsh counties. Jermyn (1827) recorded it from "*Birch Woods near Ipswich, Suffolk*" and in "*Raydon Wood on low Blackthorns.*" In Morley's annotated copy of this book had been added "*on old Blackthorn hedges mid-August and end of ditto, Higham*" (Morley, 1937a), and in the next edition Polstead was included (Jermyn, 1836).

According to Bree it had been "*Taken by Miss Berners, in woods near Ipswich*" and at Stowmarket (Greene, 1857). Postans (1858) took a female at Langham, "*a mile at least from any wood*", and Newman (1870-71) had records from near Ipswich at "*Dodnash Wood, not*

Green Hairstreak   (J. O'Sullivan)

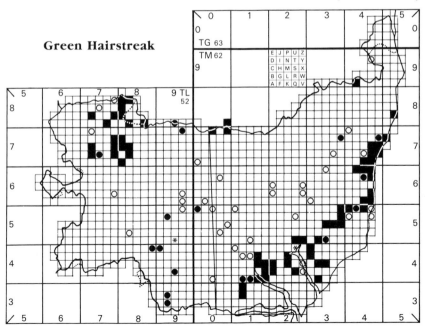

Green Hairstreak

common — W. H. Harwood" and "*Haverhill* — William Gaze".
Bloomfield (1890) considered the Brown Hairstreak to be "*Very rare*"
and knew of it from "*Saxham, A. H. W.* [*A. H. Wrattislaw*] *Raydon,
G. G.* [*G. Garrett*]" and "*Bentley, W. H.* [*W. H. Harwood*]". Tutt (1907)
lists a number of these early records and also "*Assington Thickets*" and
"*Sennage Wood, near Lavenham*", the latter almost certainly a
transcription error of Lineage Wood.

By the 1940's the Brown Hairstreak was presumed to have been long
extinct in Suffolk. That was until "*One magnificent female on 2 August
flew off Sloe-bushes just outside Bentley Woods and dropped onto a
Thistle-head*", and this at "*the very spot where W. H. Harwood of
Colchester*" and others used to take the species (Platten, 1943). The only
later Suffolk record was a specimen reared from a larva taken at Stanton,
West Suffolk by S. T. John on 3rd June 1944 [J. Heath].

The Brown Hairstreak was thought to have become extinct in Suffolk,
and remained "hidden" for over fifty years until the 1940's. Though not
seen since that time, there is a slim chance that it may again be
rediscovered in some forgotten corner.

PURPLE HAIRSTREAK *Quercusia quercus* L.

Purple Hairstreaks will often bask in the sun with wings spread, exposing
the iridescent dark purple-blue upper-side of the males, or the more
brilliant purple patches on the fore wings of the females. Usually,
however, it is the pearl-grey under-sides that catch the eye, as the
butterflies flit about the tree tops.

Widely distributed in southern Britain and the midlands, this is the
commonest of the hairstreaks in Suffolk. Morley (1937a) wrote that it
was "*Still quite abundant in all or most of our larger oak-woods*" and
this was probably an understatement. The Purple Hairstreak may be found
in most of the County's coppice woodlands where sufficient Oak
standards remain, and in the ancient park woodlands. Healthy populations
are also found associated with hedgerow and lane-side Oaks, heathland
Oak scrub, and, in the Breckland, Oak screens along the edge of conifer
plantations. It is most plentiful in the deciduous woodland and Oak scrub
of the Sandlings belt, from the south of Ipswich to as far north as
Aldeburgh, and there is even a colony in one of the Ipswich Parks.

As its Latin name suggests, the Purple Hairstreak is associated with
Oaks, and in Suffolk the Common Oak, *Quercus robur* L. is the larval
foodplant. The butterflies seldom visit flowers, but feed on the honeydew
deposited by aphids on the leaves of trees.

Because they spend much of their time hidden in the tree tops, Purple
Hairstreaks are easily overlooked, and for this reason "under-recorded".
They are best observed on warm summer evenings as late as 7.00 pm,
when they often descend to the lower branches, but under normal
circumstances a pair of binoculars is a great help when searching for
Purple Hairstreaks. In common with the other British hairstreaks there
is but one generation each year and, depending on the season, butterflies
may be seen from early July until the end of August.

Purple Hairstreak ♀　　　　　　　　　　　　　*(R. Beecroft)*

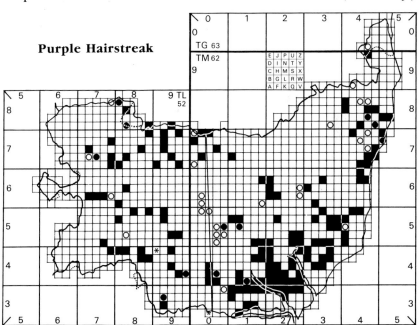

Purple Hairstreak

WHITE-LETTER HAIRSTREAK   *Strymonidia w-album*   Knoch

A small brown-black butterfly with a characteristic white line in the form of a "W" on the under-side of the hind wings, giving the species its name. In flight it appears smaller and much darker than the Purple Hairstreak. As far as is known the White-letter Hairstreak is still found widely, though very locally, in England and Wales as far north as Yorkshire (Steel, 1984), in spite of the general demise of Elm, *Ulmus* spp., the larval foodplant, as a result of the Dutch Elm Disease in the late 1970's.

This most elusive species has always been "under-recorded" in Suffolk, and the comment that it was *"Principally in the south-east of the county, rare elsewhere"* (Bloomfield, 1890), possibly reflects more accurately the distribution of entomologists at that time. The number of new colonies discovered in the Survey years masks a probable decline, resulting from the tremendous loss of Elm, and the dramatic effect this has had on the appearance of Constable's Suffolk landscape. Most of the colonies have been found in south and north-east Suffolk, and a number are thriving on sucker growth, which has developed since the death of the Elm standards. Interestingly, an elm hedgerow just outside the Borough of Ipswich supports one of the largest colonies yet found in the County, and as many as forty butterflies have been counted at one time.

The butterflies feed largely on honeydew, deposited on leaves by aphids, though they are also attracted to flowers, especially Brambles, Thistles and Privet. The White-letter Hairstreak is single brooded, on the wing in July and August. The eggs are laid on the twigs of Elm, *Ulmus* spp., which is difficult to identify to species in Suffolk because of the number of varieties and hybrids. The young larvae hatch the following spring and feed at first on flowers and then on the leaf buds and young leaves. How they survive on young Elm scrub, which apparently does not flower, is still a mystery. Hairstreaks flying about Elms are not necessarily White-letter Hairstreaks, any more than those about Oaks are Purple Hairstreaks. Both species will visit a variety of trees to feed on the honeydew on leaf surfaces.

BLACK HAIRSTREAK   *Strymonidia pruni*   L.

Following the discovery of the Black Hairstreak in Britain in 1828, records were confused with those of the White-letter Hairstreak. Both scientific and colloquial names have been muddled. The only persisting Suffolk records are those of the Rev. Joseph Greene: *"I once captured a wasted ♀ of this rare species at Brandeston"* (Greene, 1857), and *"Brandeston and Playford"* — Joseph Greene" (Newman, 1870-71). Morley (1937a) commenting on the Suffolk records, including Greene's, remarked *"All which leaves us with nasty taste in the mouth respecting the above soi-disant 'entomologists'"*. The accepted British distribution of the Black Hairstreak, between Oxford and Peterborough, also makes its presence in Suffolk seem unlikely. However, there is a genuine Suffolk connection. The original British specimens were collected by J. Seaman, a then well known Ipswich dealer in natural history specimens, in Huntingdonshire.

White-letter Hairstreak   *(B. Sawford)*

White-letter Hairstreak

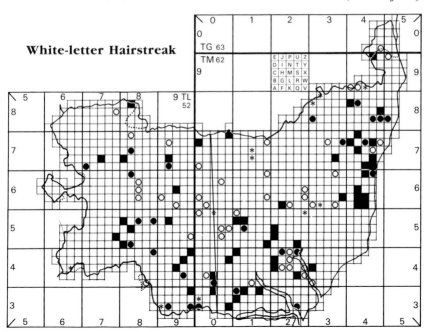

62

SMALL COPPER   *Lycaena phlaeas* L.

A very active small brown butterfly marked with brilliant metallic orange and spotted with black, the Small Copper is found the length and breadth of the country. It has always been regarded as common in Suffolk and Morley (1937a) wrote that it was *"very frequent through the whole County from Bentley, Lakenheath and Haverhill through Lavenham to Gorleston"*. Today the range of this grassland species is becoming more restricted as "waste" ground is developed, or reclaimed for agriculture. Although it may still be found along suitable roadside verges, in disused chalk and gravel pits and on coastal cliffs, the grassy heathlands of the Sandlings belt and Breck hold the largest populations. In such areas the sheltered but sunny tracks and fire-breaks left after afforestation particularly suit the species.

The first Small Coppers of the year are usually seen at the end of April, and in Suffolk there are normally three generations each year. The third brood emerges at the end of September, and during warmer autumns butterflies will still be on the wing at the end of October. It seems quite likely that some of these very late individuals represent a partial fourth brood. The eggs are laid on the larval foodplant, usually Sheep's Sorrel, *Rumex acetosella* L. or Common Sorrel, *Rumex acetosa* L., though species of Dock, *Rumex* spp. are sometimes used.

Small Coppers are attracted to various nectar flowers such as Bell Heather, Ragwort, and Yarrow, but may just as often be seen, wings open, on a bare patch of earth in full sunshine. From such a vantage point they will repeatedly pursue and drive away other butterflies, regardless of species, and their erratic darting flight makes them difficult to follow.

LARGE COPPER   *Lycaena dispar* Haw.

The British subspecies of the Large Copper, *L. dispar dispar* Haw. became extinct around the middle of the last century. It is widely accepted that the last specimen to be taken was from either Quy Fen or Bottisham in Cambridgeshire in 1851 (Dennis, 1977), but it has recently been suggested that the Large Copper may have persisted in the Norfolk Broads into the 1860's (Irwin, 1984).

The species has been recorded from *"Benacre, in Suffolk, beginning of July"* (Jermyn, 1827), and this locality was known to John Curtis who died in 1862 (Walker, 1904). Bretherton (1951a) saw an *"undoubted"* specimen *"set as an underside which was labelled 'Benacre, Suffolk about 1820'; but it was re-set in 1927 and the label is in modern handwriting"*. Although doubt has been expressed since Stephens (1828) suggested that the Benacre record might instead refer to the Purple-edged Copper, *L. hippothoë* L., it would seem on balance to be authentic. Other Suffolk records, from Woodbridge in the 1830's (Rowland Brown, 1899) discussed by Bretherton (1951a), and from *"Suffolk"* in 1860 (Barrett, 1893), dismissed by Morley (1937a), are considerably less credible.

Small Copper   *(R. Beecroft)*

Small Copper

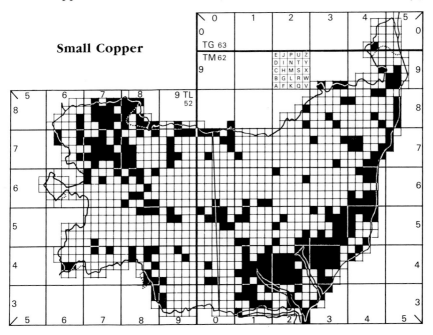

LONG-TAILED BLUE   *Lampides boeticus* L.

A strongly migratory species resident in Southern Europe, the Long-tailed Blue only very rarely reaches Britain. According to Morley (1937a), "*The late keen Lepidopterist, Mr. C. A. Pyett of Ipswich, saw a specimen of this Andalusian butterfly quite distinctly, certainly and closely, in the garden of the Bath Hotel at Felixstowe in August 1897 (teste Morley)*". We have not accepted the report from Freston (Chipperfield, 1983).

SMALL BLUE   *Cupido minimus* Fuess.

The smallest British butterfly and one of the least conspicuous, the Small Blue is easily overlooked. The males are charcoal-brown lightly powdered with silver-blue scales, and the females are dark chocolate-brown without the blue scaling.
   The Small Blue is widely distributed in Britain, but has always been a scarce insect in Suffolk. It was at one time established in three areas where chalk soils favour the growth of Kidney Vetch, *Anthyllis vulneraria* L., the larval foodplant. These were the chalk of the far west of the County, the Gipping Valley, and the Breckland, where there are records for "*Brandon Warren*" (Jermyn, 1827), Tuddenham (Bloomfield, 1890), and Mildenhall (Tutt, 1909). It was still found in Breckland in the 1930's (Anon, 1932). There are many records of Small Blue from "*Newmarket*", but the majority should be assigned to the Devil's Ditch, Cambridgeshire. Slightly to the north, according to Morley (1937a), it was "*taken annually at Worlington about 1900 (Sparke)*" and seven were seen amongst its foodplant "*in a chalk-pit at Worlington in late June 1890 (Norgate)*". In the Gipping Valley it was found "*Between Needham and Ipswich*" by H. Lingwood (Bloomfield, 1890), and in the same general area was "*not uncommon, especially in 1920, on the Creeting Hills and Coddenham chalk-pit (Platten)*" (Morley, 1937a). It was seen regularly in this area just outside Stowmarket "*during the late 1940's up to the mid-1950's but then declining with the last record in 1959*" [T. C. Rednall].
   Outside these areas, Ellis (1984) wrote that "*in the drought summer of 1921 I caught one from a pavement outside my house at Gorleston*". Another was seen in Bishop Whittingham's "*Ipswich garden in August 1933*" (Morley, 1937a) and just outside Ipswich in the early 1950's there was a small colony on a site now destroyed at Warren Heath [D. A. Young]. There was also a colony near Dunwich in the early 1950's (Anon, 1952), and a specimen taken by B. A. Coney in 1952 survives [H. E. Jenner].
   The Small Blue is on the wing at the end of May and in June, and in warm summers there is a partial second brood in August and early September. It forms small colonies in sheltered, sunny situations such as chalk pits and railway cuttings, where the larval foodplant grows. There are many such sites in Suffolk, especially in the west, and it is quite possible that undiscovered colonies still survive.

*SHORT-TAILED BLUE   *Everes argiades* Pallas

SILVER-STUDDED BLUE   *Plebejus argus* L.

A most attractive little butterfly, especially the male with its black bordered, violet-blue upper-side and white wing fringes. The slightly smaller female is dark brown with various amounts of orange along the wing edges. In both sexes the under-side black spots around the outer margin of the hind wings are "studded" with metallic silver blue scales, giving the species its name.

The Silver-studded Blue is a variable butterfly and recognisable forms have developed in different parts of its British range. The most extreme, variously described as subspecies or races, are *masseyi* Tutt, once found on the mosses of Lancashire and Westmorland, *caernensis* Thomps. still found in the Great Ormes Head area of North Wales, and the southern chalk and limestone form, *cretaceus* Tutt. Other races and subspecies have been proposed and include populations found on the Sandlings of East Suffolk which, according to Worms (1952), were *"quite distinct from the heath form prevalent in the southern counties"*, mainly on account of their *"large size and tendency of the females to blueness"*. Whatever the taxonomic rank of these forms, the differences and the range of habitat types used by separate populations make the Silver-studded Blue an extremely interesting butterfly.

Although not yet a nationally rare species, the Silver-studded Blue is declining alarmingly. In Suffolk it used to be found across much of the Breckland, at various sites on the Sandlings, and in scattered colonies well outside these areas. Morley (1937a) wrote *"its headquarters with us, however, are upon the Breck where it abounds from Brandon to Tuddenham as freely as in the New Forest or at Oxshott"*. It was last seen in the Breckland in 1965 at Barton Mills [J. L. Fenn] and the less than a dozen colonies left in Suffolk are all in the Sandlings area.

It is interesting that the Silver-studded Blue was once found in several very different types of habitat in Suffolk. Sandlings colonies today are usually located in sheltered sunny areas where the heathland succession has produced a habitat mosaic of Ling, *Calluna vulgaris* (L.) Hull, Bell Heather, *Erica cinerea* L., short turf and bare ground. The Breckland heath colonies are said to have been similar, but without the Bell Heather. Silver-studded Blues were once also found on Redgrave Fen, most likely on the wet heath area where Cross-leaved Heath, *Erica tetralix* L. grows in abundance, and there were several grassland colonies without any of the heathers. One such colony *"existed in the corner of some grassy parkland"* at Nowton until 1948 [R. F. Eley] and another on low meadowland near Stowmarket until the early 1960's [T. C. Rednall].

The larvae have been reported to feed on a wide variety of foodplants in captivity, including Ling, Bell Heather, Cross-leaved Heath, Gorse, *Ulex* spp., Bird's-foot Trefoil, *Lotus corniculatus* L., Bird's-foot, *Ornithopus perpusillus* L. and Rockrose, *Helianthemum nummularium* (L.) Mill. However, wild larvae have yet to be found in Suffolk, and an intensive search by night and by day failed to reveal any at known localities. The larvae have a honey gland and are "milked" by ants, *Lasius* spp., but the precise nature of the relationship is not known, and they can be reared in captivity well away from ants.

Mr. E. Parsons has spent many hours observing Silver-studded Blues in the wild. Before laying each egg the female performs a number of "dummy runs", curling her abdomen around a plant, and dipping the tip under a leaf or onto a leaf surface; a behaviour likely to trick the unwary observer. Although "dummy runs" were frequently made on Ling, rather surprisingly the only plant on which females were seen to lay was Bracken, *Pteridium aquilinum* (L.) Kuhn. The pearl-white eggs were placed singly on the underside of the pinnules, usually between 120 and 450 mm from the ground. A search with Mr. Parsons at another colony revealed numerous eggs on encroaching Bracken, but none on known foodplants! This could be a type of "edge bias", noted in quite a number of butterfly species (Dennis, 1984). As the Bracken died back in the autumn the pinnules curled round the eggs and formed a natural shroud. The study continues and perhaps next year we shall discover what happens to the young larvae on hatching from the eggs in spring. It is most unlikely that they will attempt to feed on Bracken. Egg laying has also been seen on the woody stems of Ling and under the leaves of Bell Heather [N. Ravenscroft]. There is a single generation each year and the males, which emerge a short time before the females, may be seen from late June onwards. A few ragged individuals are sometimes still on the wing in late August. Bell Heather seems to be the most important nectar flower, but towards the evenings Silver-studded Blues will perch conspicuously, head downwards and wings positioned to catch the last rays of the sun, near the extremities of the larger clumps of Ling. They become more torpid as darkness approaches, and as many as twenty individuals may roost communally on a single heather clump. Mating was most frequently observed in the late afternoon, and butterflies would sit *in cop.* on top of plants for long periods, and would even roost in this position.

There are many reasons for the decline of the Silver-studded Blue in Suffolk. Heath reclamation and fragmentation, urban development and afforestation have all played a part and the effects of Bracken and scrub encroachment after the introduction of myxomatosis should not be underestimated (Worms, 1959). In recent years the greatest threat has been the development of heathland on the Ipswich eastern fringe, and actually during the Survey years final permission was given to build on a part of Martlesham Heath supporting Suffolk's strongest colony. The Silver-studded Blue forms distinct colonies and prefers heathland at an early successional stage or that stabilised by rabbit grazing. During the Survey one colony moved approximately 30 m each year into an area recovering from a heathland fire, but others seem to have changed little since the 1960's. Individuals are occasionally found well away from known colonies [E. Parsons], but heathland fragmentation has made it unlikely that natural recolonisation of suitable areas will take place to any great extent.

Silver-studded Blues at communal roost *(R. Beecroft)*

Silver-studded Blue ♀ *(R. Beecroft)*

Silver-studded Blue

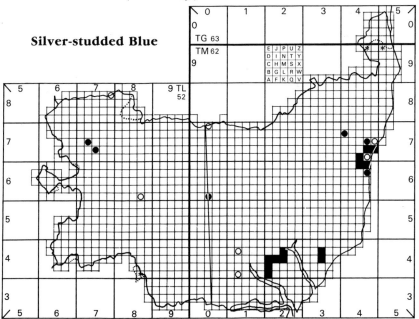

BROWN ARGUS *Aricia agestis* D. & S.

A small, inconspicuous butterfly, chocolate-brown on the upper-side, with a series of orange spots around the outer wing margins, and a black spot near the centre of the fore wings. The Brown Argus is very easily confused with both the brown form of the female Common Blue and the female Silver-studded Blue.

Widely distributed in lowland areas of southern and midland Britain as far north as Lincolnshire and North Wales, this species has an interesting distribution in Suffolk. It was regarded as *"Scarce and local"* by Greene (1857) and *"Not common but widely distributed"* by Bloomfield (1890), an assessment with which Morley (1937a) concurred. Today the stronghold of the Brown Argus is undoubtedly the Breckland, where it prefers sheltered, sunny sites such as grassy banks or the fire-breaks and tracks in conifer areas. Away from the Breck it is almost confined to the chalk area of the Gipping Valley, but was formerly more widespread and even used to be found regularly in some of the south Suffolk woodlands.

The Brown Argus has two generations each year and is on the wing from mid-May until the end of June in normal seasons, and again from late July until early September. It is a butterfly of rough grassland on poor soils, and the larvae feed on Rock Rose, *Helianthemum nummularium* (L.) Mill. and Common Storksbill, *Erodium cicutarium* (L.) L'Hérit. Rock Rose is now a scarce species in Suffolk and has all but disappeared in the east. The larvae must feed on Storksbill or some as yet unrecognised foodplant in the majority of the Suffolk colonies. Although an experienced observer can recognise Brown Argus on the wing by their characteristic flight showing the silver-grey underside, they are still likely to have been overlooked, and are probably "under-recorded." A search of rough grassland in disused gravel and chalk pits, railway cuttings and along the coast will probably lead to the discovery of new colonies.

NORTHERN BROWN ARGUS *Aricia artaxerxes* Fabr.

Smart (1918) wrote; *"I have in my collection three specimens of* Aricia medon, *ab.* artaxerxes, *that were taken by the late Dr. David Smart on Lakenheath Warren, Suffolk some time in the sixties. He told me that this form, which I believe was then considered specifically distinct, was during one season not uncommon in a very limited locality on the Warren"*.

Lakenheath is so far south and east of other British localities that this record cannot be accepted, unless the specimens in question can be traced, and their identity confirmed. The white spot on the fore wing was at that time the principal character separating the Northern Brown Argus and Brown Argus. Rarely the Brown Argus also has a white spot and perhaps the Lakenheath butterflies were of this type. We have so far been unable to locate Smart's specimens, if they still exist, to remove any element of doubt.

Brown Argus ♀   *(B. Sawford)*

Brown Argus

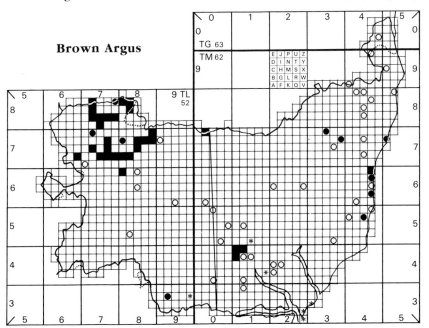

COMMON BLUE   *Polyommatus icarus*   Rott.

Male Common Blues are the brightest blue butterflies found in Suffolk. Freshly emerged specimens are responsible for all recent reports of the now extinct Adonis Blue, which is even more brilliant but has the white wing fringes marked with black opposite the vein endings. The females are extremely variable and range in colour from dark chocolate-brown with orange marks around the wing margins to almost entirely blue, again with orange marginal spots. The brown females are easily confused with the Brown Argus or female Silver-studded Blues, and a good identification guide should always be consulted to resolve any doubt.

The Common Blue is found throughout the British Isles, and has been common and widespread in Suffolk since recording began. It was *"Very common"* towards the end of the last century (Bloomfield, 1890), and Morley (1937a) wrote that *"it occurs everywhere"*. Although widespread and usually numerous where it occurs, its distribution in Suffolk today is somewhat more restricted than it used to be. It has become very local in the most intensive arable areas such as north central Suffolk and is most plentiful on the heathlands and heathland edges of the Breckland and Sandlings. It remains easily the most common "blue" in Suffolk.

The Common Blue is a butterfly of well-grazed turf and grassland on poor soils and disturbed ground. Favourite haunts outside the heathlands are coastal cliffs and areas of fixed shingle, chalk and gravel pits, road and railway cuttings and embankments and derelict land, even in urban areas. It is in these types of situation that the larval foodplant Bird's-foot Trefoil, *Lotus corniculatus* L. thrives. The eggs are laid on the upper surface of young leaves, and in common with those of many other "blues" mature larvae have a honey gland and are usually attended by ants. Other foodplants include Restharrow, *Ononis* spp., Lesser Yellow Trefoil, *Trifolium dubium* Sibth. and related species. There are two generations of butterflies each year, and they may be seen at any time between the end of May and late September.

CHALK HILL BLUE   *Lysandra coridon*   Poda

A butterfly of rough grassland in chalk and limestone areas of southern Britain where Horseshoe Vetch, *Hippocrepis comosa* L. the larval foodplant is found. Though still widespread, the Chalk Hill Blue has become considerably more local over the years, as pastures are "improved" or have become overgrown.

In Suffolk the Chalk Hill Blue was first known from *"Chalk-pits, Little Blakenham"* (Jermyn, 1824), and persisted in the Blakenham area almost to the turn of the century. It was last recorded from the *"Blakenham Parva chalk-pits, early in August 1891 (Capt. Hill) and in 1895 (Platten)"* (Morley, 1937a). C. R. Bree took the species nearby, *"on Creeting Hills, August 14, 1856"* (Greene, 1857), and no doubt it was to be found at one time in other suitable localities along the Gipping Valley where the chalk comes to the surface.

Common Blue ♀   *(J. D. Bakewell)*

Common Blue

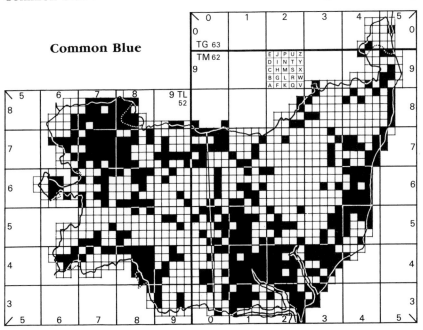

The Chalk Hill Blue is also known to have occurred at *"Moulton and Eriswell"* (Jermyn, 1827), *"Newmarket, Dalham, Tuddenham, Felixstowe, Lowestoft"* (Bloomfield, 1890), and *"Bury St Edmunds (Norgate)"* (Tutt, 1910). A series of sixteen specimens labelled from Barton Mills on 9 August 1923, in the J. B. Garner-Richards Collection at the Norwich Castle Museum, is all we know of the species in Suffolk this century. However, it must have strayed onto Newmarket Heath from time to time, from the well known colony along the Devil's Ditch, just over the border in Cambridgeshire, and this was no doubt where Postans (1858) took it *"in boundless profusion just on the borders of Cambridgeshire, but in Suffolk"*.

ADONIS BLUE *Lysandra bellargus* Rott.

Another grassland butterfly confined to the chalk and limestone areas of southern England. The larvae feed on the Horseshoe Vetch, *Hippocrepis comosa* L., as do those of the Chalk Hill Blue, but the Adonis Blue prefers more heavily grazed sites and is double brooded.

The Adonis Blue has been extinct in Suffolk for over 100 years. Jermyn (1827) recorded the species then known as the Clifden Blue from *"Moulton and Dalham"*, though Bloomfield (1890) thought this was *"Probably an error"*. He did not, however, know that there was also a record from nearby Newmarket: *"Several specimens were taken at Newmarket by Mr. Wagstaff many years ago"* (Miller and Skertchley, 1878), and we can find no good reason to doubt the records. Hind (1889) lists Newmarket Heath and Dalham amongst the West Suffolk localities for the foodplant, and all three sites are on the chalk in the same area.

MAZARINE BLUE *Cyaniris semiargus* Rott.

Though still widespread and in places common on the Continent, the Mazarine Blue is now extinct in Britain. It was a species of hay meadows and rough ground where the larval foodplant, Red Clover, *Trifolium pratense* L. was to be found. Records show that it was widespread but very local in southern England as far north as Yorkshire, in the first half of the 19th century (Dale, 1902), and there has been no satisfactory explanation of the butterfly's disappearance. Six specimens from Glamorgan in 1877 are generally regarded as the last "natives" to have been taken (Bretherton, 1951a).

G. Garrett made the only known pre-1877 Suffolk capture, near Ipswich at *"Foxhall Heath, one specimen June 24th, 1861"* (Bloomfield, 1890). The origin of the specimens taken *"about Woodbridge"* (Rowland Brown, 1899) relies too much on hearsay, and the record cannot be accepted. The following note in *Country-side* is difficult to explain satisfactorily:-

> *"One of the last authentic localities for mazarine blue is Gorleston, near Yarmouth. Two were taken in 1900 and three*

Chalk Hill Blue ♂   *(B. Sawford)*

Adonis Blue ♂   *(B. Sawford)*

in 1901, etc. These specimens like the very rare hawk moths, are probably either blown over from the Continent themselves, or are descendants of such".

(Anon, 1908)

The Gorleston insects are, as the note suggests, generally regarded as products of chance migration or perhaps accidental introduction.

HOLLY BLUE   *Celastrina argiolus* L.

The lilac-tinted blue males with black edged fore wings could be confused with some of the other "blues," but black tipped fore wings make the females unmistakable. The under-side in both sexes is a distinctive pale grey-blue with small black spots, totally lacking the orange markings of otherwise similar species. The upper-side of the second brood females is more broadly and heavily marked with black.

The Holly Blue is widely distributed in Britain, but becomes uncommon towards the north of England. In Suffolk it appears to have been somewhat scarce in the 19th century to the extent that Bree could only cite a single record; *"Taken by Mr. Levett, in Finborough Park, but not the last year or two"* (Greene, 1857). Even towards the end of the century it was considered *"Local, and generally somewhat rare"* (Bloomfield, 1890), but Morley (1937a) gives the impression that by the 1930's it had become more numerous and widespread. However, dramatic population fluctuations are well known in the Holly Blue and make assessment of the underlying trends extremely difficult. Goldsmith (1952-3) commenting on the species' fortunes in Suffolk attributed population crashes to early spring emergence followed by unpredictable weather, often resulting in low breeding success. Other writers have related crashes to parasitism. There can be little doubt that during the Survey years the Holly Blue experienced a succession of favourable seasons, and as a result was widely reported.

Today the species is widely but locally distributed throughout Suffolk. It frequents well-established hedgerows, woodland rides and edges, urban parks and suburban gardens. The Holly Blue is especially common in areas of mature gardens in Ipswich, and in the older parks such as Christchurch and Holywells. In these areas there is a plentiful supply of the larval foodplants, Holly, *Ilex aquifolium* L. and Ivy, *Hedera helix* L. Spring Holly Blues lay their eggs at the base of the flower buds of Holly and the larvae feed on the buds, young leaves and developing berries. Larvae from eggs laid by the second brood feed on the buds and developing berries of Ivy. This alternation of foodplants is unique amongst British butterflies. Other foodplants sometimes used include Dogwood, *Cornus sanguinea* L., Spindle, *Euonymus europaeus* L., Gorse, *Ulex europaeus* L., Bramble, *Rubus* spp. and Snowberry, *Symphoricarpos rivularis* Suksdorf, and Suffolk's largest known population at Landguard Point near Felixstowe thrives in an area where there is no Holly. H. E. Chipperfield once found many young larvae feeding on raspberries, *Rubus idaeus* L. in his Stowmarket garden (Vinter, 1946).

Holly Blue ♀ *(M. O'Brien)*

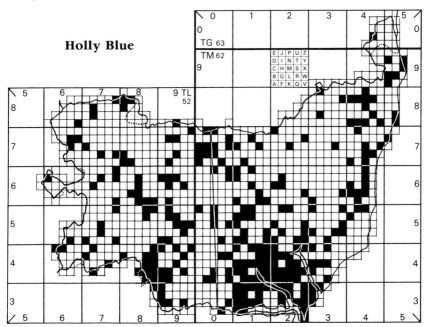

The first generation of the year is on the wing from late April, but has been recorded in Suffolk as early as March. This is long before the first Common Blues are usually seen, and it is safe to assume that a "blue" seen before the middle of May will be a Holly Blue. This generation is over by the middle of June and the summer butterflies may be seen from the middle of July until the end of September. Holly Blues, apparently in fresh condition, were seen at Landguard between 27th October and 1st November 1984 [H. R. Beecroft and D. R. Moore]. These raise the possibility of a partial third brood, which would be quite exceptional.

Holly Blues have been noted on a variety of different nectar flowers, including Spanish Bluebell and Lilac in the spring, and Bramble in the summer. As many as a dozen have been seen together on a clump of Spanish Bluebells at Landguard taking nectar, and butterflies have also been reported probing damp mud at the edge of Alton Water [M. C. Marsh] and bird droppings.

*LARGE BLUE   *Maculinea arion* L.

DUKE OF BURGUNDY FRITILLARY   *Hamearis lucina* L.

Not a true fritillary, but the only British representative of a group known as the "metalmarks". The Duke of Burgundy is essentially a woodland species, preferring the sheltered parts of clearings and glades, but is equally at home amongst scrub on chalk and limestone grassland. The larvae feed on Cowslip, *Primula veris* L. or Primrose, *Primula vulgaris* L. and the butterflies are on the wing in the latter half of May and early June.

The Duke of Burgundy Fritillary is widely distributed in England, though usually very local, and most common on chalk areas to the south. It was recorded from "*Hintlesham, Suff.*" by Jermyn (1824) and according to Bree it was "*In various woods; not very common*" (Greene, 1857), but Postans (1858) "*got a very fine series*" at Raydon in 1850. Stainton (1857) had information that it was common at Stowmarket, and "*Near Stowmarket* — H. H. Crewe" and "*Brandeston and Playford* — Joseph Greene" are given as localities by Newman (1870-71). Bloomfield (1890) considered the species "*Very local*" and lists as localities: Needham (H. Lingwood), Raydon (W. Harwood), and Freston (A. C. Freeman and W. H. Collins). Bentley was thought by Morley (1937a) to be the species' headquarters in Suffolk "*up to at least 1899*", though it must also have been still plentiful at Raydon Wood, and a series of six in the General Collection at Ipswich Museum taken by J. H. Hocking on 26th May 1898, is testimony to this. It was still to be found in Raydon Wood in 1930 (Gilles, 1932) but "*three especial expeditions*" to the area in 1947 "*on 17, 24, 28 May failed to discover traces*" (Vinter, 1947). The only later record from Suffolk is of "*several freshly emerged*" on 12th May 1973, at Bradfield Woods [M. Chinery] but there is some suspicion that these may have been introduced. The Duke of Burgundy Fritillary is not a mobile species and it is unlikely to occur naturally again in the County.

Duke of Burgundy Fritillary   *(B. Sawford)*

WHITE ADMIRAL   *Ladoga camilla* L.

This most distinctive butterfly with a black-brown upper-side and striking white markings cannot be mistaken for any other, except perhaps the Purple Emperor. The intricate orange-brown, black and white under-side is particularly attractive.

   The history of the White Admiral in Britain is characterised by marked contractions and expansions in range, which Pollard (1979) attributes to a combination of habitat change and weather. Today it is widely distributed in the south and south midlands, and has been recorded as far north as Lincolnshire (Heath *et al.*, 1984). It was not known in Suffolk to Jermyn (1824-1833) or Paget (1834), and must have been scarce at that time, but soon after it was recorded from the woodlands in the south-east of the County, centred on the Bentley/Belstead area to the south of Ipswich. Bree knew the species to be "*Common in woods near Ipswich and Stowmarket*" (Greene, 1857) and this situation had changed little by the time Bloomfield (1890) wrote that it was "*Local, sometimes abundant. Stoke by Nayland, Stowmarket, Bentley, and various places near Ipswich*". There were occasional reports of unusual abundance in some seasons, and Morley (1933) had "*a note showing no less than 464 specimens to have been slaughtered by workingmen-collectors in a single south-east wood [Bentley area] during the year 1900 alone!*". It is interesting that the White Admiral was at a low ebb nationally at this time

(Heath *et al.*, 1984). In Suffolk the species remained confined to the south-east, and at Bentley Woods was said by Morley (1920) to still *"survive as of yore"*.

The status remained unchanged until the early 1930's, when White Admirals started to be reported from woodlands across the County. A period of relative abundance followed and they could be found in many of Suffolk's ancient woodlands until the late 1950's or early 1960's, when followed a sharp decline in their fortunes. They then became extremely scarce, and even disappeared from the woodlands to the south of Ipswich.

In the late 1960's came the first reports of White Admirals from the County's extensive areas of conifer plantation, and today the species is found almost exclusively in these, and in a few largely "coniferised" ancient woodlands. The very few exceptions are heathland sites with extensive Birch and Oak scrub, and a single coppice woodland, Bradfield Woods, from which it now seems to have disappeared. The wide open ride systems developed by the foresters favour the species, even as the conifer blocks mature, and a good growth of the larval foodplant Honeysuckle, *Lonicera periclymenum* L. develops along the perimeters. This butterfly is one of the few on the increase in Suffolk, and 1985 saw the first reports from the Mildenhall plantations [D. J. L. Agassiz].

The single brood of the White Admiral is usually on the wing from early July until mid-August, but in early seasons butterflies may be about in June and stragglers are sometimes seen into September. The eggs are laid on the leaves of Honeysuckle, and the larvae feed only for a short time and, while still small, spin a partly eaten leaf into a tunnel in which to spend the winter. These remain on the plant through the winter and are not difficult to find when many of the other leaves have been shed.

It is a pleasure to watch the graceful flight of White Admirals as they glide amongst the trees, or descend to take nectar from Bramble flowers. They tend to be less active and are best viewed in the late afternoon. It still seems strange to watch these butterflies alighting on the fronds of conifers.

PURPLE EMPEROR *Apatura iris* L.

One of the largest and most handsome of the British butterflies, the Purple Emperor is, unfortunately, still sought after by collectors. The females are larger, but lack the iridescent purple-blue sheen of the males, which makes them so attractive.

The Purple Emperor is a woodland species, still widely distributed though generally rare in the south midlands and southern counties, but no longer found in Suffolk. It was last recorded here in 1959, though there are a very few unconfirmed sightings since that time, some of which were almost certainly misidentified White Admirals.

In the 19th century the Purple Emperor was quite common in Suffolk. It was known from Badley (Jermyn, 1824), *"Hull, Old Hall, Dodnash and Raydon Woods"* (Jermyn, 1827); and was *"tolerably abundant in*

White Admiral   *(R. Beecroft)*

White Admiral

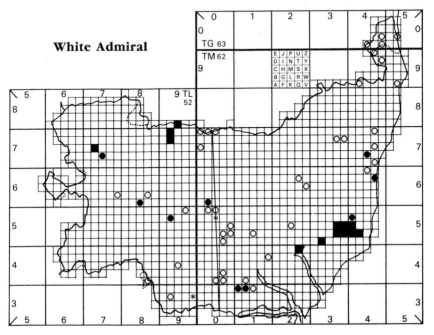

Raydon Wood [where] I once got eight larvae in one day" (Postans, 1858). There are records from Stowmarket (Stainton, 1857), *"Bentley, Coombs, etc.* H. H. Crewe; *Redisham and Worlingham Parks* — W. M. Crowfoot, *in Old-hall Wood very rare, Haverhill* — William Gaze; *[and] Assington Wood, near Sudbury* — John Grubb" (Newman, 1870-71). In addition to these Morley (1937a) knew of a specimen taken at Waldringfield in 1878 in the collection of A. P. Waller, and a record from Needham Market, attributed to H. Lingwood.

Newman (1870-71), repeating an earlier note in the *Entomologist*, wrote that it was *"so common near Ipswich in 1868 that many of our collectors have taken eight or ten dozen each* — Garrett Garrett". Perhaps an exaggeration, and the account by Frohawk (1934b) that Garrett *"made the sensational capture of no less than sixteen male and two female Purple Emperors"* and that *"other local collectors at that time also took proportionately many specimens"* is more accurate. Garrett took his specimens on *"a Mountain-ash at Bentley Woods"*, where Frohawk (1941) remembered *"in the hot July of 1881, there watching five* Iris *playing about the top of an Oak."*

By the turn of the century it had become rarer in Suffolk, though still survived in its old haunts. In the woods to the south of Ipswich the Purple Emperor was seen *"flying high among the leaves of an oak-tree in Bentley Woods"* in 1933 (Butters, 1934), again in 1935 (Morley 1937a), nearby at Belstead in 1940 (Simpson, 1940), and finally at Bentley in 1941 (Webster, 1941). Interestingly one was seen in Ipswich itself, at Christchurch Park in 1933 (Spencer, 1933). *"Mr. Bernard Harwood bred two males from larvae that he had taken in Raydon Wood during the early summer of 1919"* (Gilles, 1934) and the species was seen there on a number of occasions in the 1950's and finally in 1959, when two eggs were collected and reared, producing two males (Beaufoy 1960 and 1970).

The few 20th century sightings away from the woodlands of the south-east of the County are; *"A very ragged ♂ taken (on rotten rabbit guts!) 29 September"*, 1946 at St. Olaves [H. E. Jenner], one seen *"in the woods at or close to Walpole during July 1946"* (Morley, 1948) and a male seen at Nowton in 1947 [R. F. Eley].

Purple Emperors are on the wing from the second week of July and throughout August, and spend much of their time above the tree tops. They are, however, attracted to carrion and animal droppings and such baits have long been used to tempt them by collectors. Beaufoy (1953) describes how a *"male Purple Emperor was seen feeding from the decaying flesh"* of a dead hedgehog hung up for the purpose in Raydon Wood. Adults on emergence tend to gather round a particular tree, often an Oak (the "master Oak") though not necessarily so, and here pairing takes place, and the aerial dog-fights of the males may be seen. The females lay their eggs on the leaves of Sallows, *Salix caprea* L. or *S. cinerea* L., in sheltered areas, often along rides, and it is on these bushes that the unusual horned larvae feed.

The Purple Emperor may be found in a variety of woodland types and is increasingly found in conifer woodlands. Perhaps one day it will again be seen in Suffolk.

Purple Emperor ♂   *(B. Sawford)*

Purple Emperor

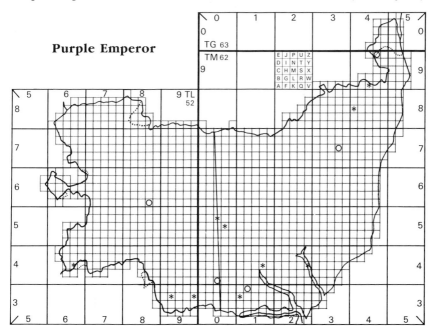

RED ADMIRAL   *Vanessa atalanta* L.

The large size and striking black, white and scarlet wings of the Red Admiral make it a conspicuous butterfly, hardly likely to be overlooked or mistaken for any other. Because it is such a familiar "British" butterfly, it is not always appreciated that the number in this country depends almost entirely on the arrival of migrants from Southern Europe each spring.

The Red Admiral is one of Britain's most regular migrant species and may be seen anywhere in the country. It has always been regarded as common in Suffolk, though numbers vary from year to year. During the Survey many were seen in both 1983 and 85, but it was generally scarce throughout 1984. Red Admirals normally arrive in Suffolk towards the end of May or in June, but often there are much earlier reports, in April or sometimes in March. Even in the poor year of 1984 one was seen on 22nd March at Bromeswell [A. Hubbard], and it is quite possible that some of these early butterflies may have survived the winter in hibernation. Morley (1937a) wrote that one was *"Once found hibernating in a disused water-mill in the Beccles marshes"*, but whether or not a few manage to survive our winters, there is no doubt that relative abundance is determined by immigration.

Red Admirals seem to prefer lightly wooded areas and are often seen in parkland and mature gardens. The map shows how widely distributed this mobile species is, but the coastal bias is probably real.

Eggs are laid on the larval foodplants, usually Stinging Nettle, *Urtica dioica* L. but occasionally Hop, *Humulus lupulus* L. or Pellitory-of-the-Wall, *Parietaria diffusa* Mert. & Koch, and there may be two generations of home-bred butterflies in a season. Red Admiral numbers build up throughout the summer and reach their peak in late August or September. At this time of the year they are common visitors to gardens and orchards, attracted by the flowers of Buddleia and Michaelmas Daisies, or over-ripe pears and plums. In wilder places they are more likely to be attracted to sap runs on damaged trees, or to the flowers of Ivy, and sometimes they take the nectar in such quantities that they become "drunk" and can be picked up by hand with ease.

There is now considerable evidence of a southward migration in the autumn, and at the Bird Observatory at Landguard Point southerly movements have frequently been recorded. On 25th September 1985, Red Admirals were seen to arrive from the north and depart to the south throughout the day. They fed on the flowers of Ivy cladding the walls of the old fort, but within an hour of the maximum count of forty butterflies, reached early in the afternoon, numbers were halved. Similar observations were made to the south, in Essex, where Earey (1977) recorded *"upwards of 90 individual butterflies flying purposefully across the sea wall and moving due south"* in October.

Red Admirals at Ivy blossom   *(H. R. Beecroft)*

Red Admiral

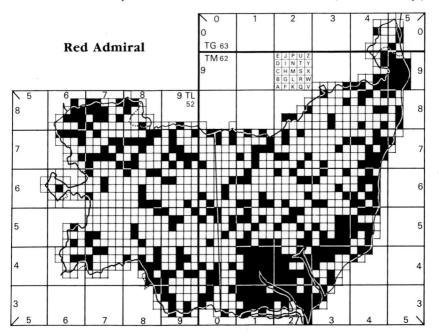

PAINTED LADY *Cynthia cardui* L.

An unmistakable butterfly with white spotted, black tipped fore wings similar to the Red Admiral, but otherwise pale orange to bright salmon-pink with brown-black markings. The Painted Lady is another of the migrants from Southern Europe and North Africa.

It may be seen in favourable seasons throughout Britain, but more frequently in the south. In Suffolk a few at least are recorded most years and large numbers appear quite regularly. This no doubt accounts for the apparently conflicting comments of our early entomologists. Paget (1834) writing from north-east Suffolk stated that the Painted Lady was *"more or less abundant in different years,"* but to Bree it was *"Not common."* (Greene, 1857). Bloomfield (1890) could have been describing the present status when he wrote that the species was *"Periodical but often common."* In the Survey years the Painted Lady was plentiful in 1983 and again in 1985, especially in the late summer, when several readers' letters appeared in the local press, noting the occurrence of this attractive butterfly in their gardens. Very few were seen in 1984, a poor year for many of our migrant species. According to Morley (1937a) *"None, or practically so, were seen throughout Suffolk from June 1894 to September 1903,"* and none were seen inland at Monk Soham *"throughout the decade preceding 1914."* It would be most unusual these days for such periods to pass without Painted Ladies being seen.

It is usually early June before the first of the year's Painted Ladies arrive in Suffolk, but exceptionally a much earlier immigration occurs. In 1952 *"During the last days of February a few Painted Ladies. . . appeared on the South coast to be reinforced by an almost unprecedented immigration of these butterflies during the first days of March"* (Worms, 1952-53). It was a little later that the first was seen in Suffolk at Thorpeness on 16th March (Garnett, 1952), and Waller (1952-3) saw one in his Waldringfield garden on 18th April, another on May 6th and *"by the 9th they were flying in dozens on a lilac hedge"*. In 1985 a similar immigration took place and early butterflies were seen at Minsmere on 4th April [Mrs. L. Charlton], and Offton on 9th April [H. Barnett], followed by many others. Unfortunately, because of the poor weather, numbers did not really build up until the late summer and early autumn. Unlike the Red Admiral, the Painted Lady prefers more open habitat and the map indicates that individuals may appear anywhere, but are most frequently seen along the coastal belt.

Although wide ranging and powerful flyers, Painted Ladies will often take up territories and patrol some chosen piece of ground or length of track. Thistles, *Carduus* and *Cirsium* spp. are the usual larval foodplants, but Viper's Bugloss, *Echium vulgare* L., Stinging Nettle, *Urtica dioica* L. and Burdock, *Arctium* spp. are amongst others sometimes eaten. There is at least one, and possibly two generations of butterflies in a season, and if the weather is favourable a few may still be seen in November.

* **AMERICAN PAINTED LADY** *Cynthia virginiensis* Drury

Painted Lady   *(A. Beaumont)*

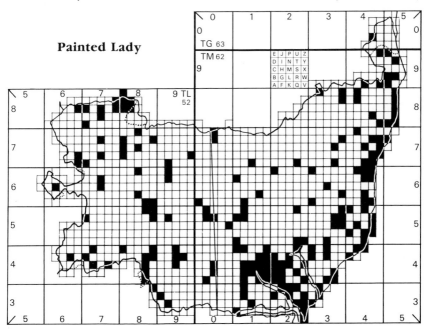

Painted Lady

SMALL TORTOISESHELL   *Aglais urticae* L.

Also known as the "King George" in Suffolk because of its majestic appearance, the Small Tortoiseshell is certainly one of the most attractive British butterflies. The under side is a dull mottled brown, providing excellent camouflage when at rest against bark or old timber.

The ubiquitous Small Tortoiseshell is found throughout Britain and Ireland, and is perhaps the most familiar of all our butterflies. It has not been regarded as anything but common in Suffolk since recording began, and today must be present in every tetrad. It overwinters as a butterfly in the dark corner of an outbuilding or church, and is one of the earliest species on the wing. First records of the year are usually of butterflies flapping against window panes trying to escape from their winter retreat, sometimes as early as January, but it is usually April before many are seen. Populations fluctuate, and in 1983 a brief, warm, sunny spell at the beginning of April brought the Small Tortoiseshells out of hibernation, only to be followed by cold, wet weather. Many must have been killed before they could breed and numbers were well below average all year, but very quickly returned to normal in 1984.

Eggs are laid in April or May in large batches on the under-side of the terminal leaves of the Stinging Nettle, *Urtica dioica* L. or Small Nettle, *Urtica urens* L., two very common and widespread species. The larvae feed communally, in a web, and only separate after their final moult. These larvae produce the summer generation of butterflies in late June or July, and there is a second brood in August and September. The Small Tortoiseshell is especially common in gardens in the late summer, attracted to the flowers of Buddleia, Ice Plants and Michaelmas Daisies.

Migration in this species is poorly understood, but there are several records of butterflies coming in from over the sea. On 26th July 1933, "*M. B. Ellis, stationed at the end of Gorleston Pier between 1.30 and 7 pm., witnessed the arrival of about a dozen* " (Frohawk, 1934a), and a "*very large number* " were seen "*coming in from the sea at Gunton [Lowestoft] on September 25th*", 1969 (Anon, 1969).

LARGE TORTOISESHELL   *Nymphalis polychloros* L.

This species is liable to be confused with the much commoner Small Tortoiseshell, and is best recognised by the black spot on the hind wings (rather than a black wing base), the "extra spot" on the fore wings, the duller orange-brown colour and larger size.

Populations of the Large Tortoiseshell in Britain are known to have fluctuated widely over the decades, and the species is now at such a low ebb that it is "*not known for certain. . . that any resident populations. . . survive*" (Heath *et al.,* 1984). It has been suggested that the Large Tortoiseshell was never a true resident, but a migrant sustaining itself over several favourable seasons at a time. However, an analysis of its history and life-history in Suffolk, and the absence of records from Ireland, argue strongly against this conclusion.

87

Small Tortoiseshell   *(A. Beaumont)*

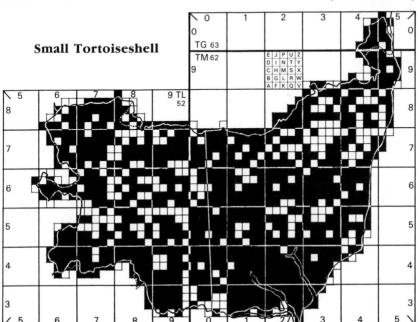

Jermyn (1824) recorded the species (then known as the Wood Large Tortoiseshell) from *"Bentley, Suffolk"* and Greene (1857) states that in Suffolk it was *"Common, both in the spring and the close of summer. Larvae in profusion on elms"*. According to Newman (1870-71) it was *"Generally distributed"* in Suffolk, and in 1872 and 1873, Frohawk found it *"in abundance in the neighbourhood of Ipswich"* (Frohawk, 1937). Bloomfield (1890) considered it *"Generally distributed and common"*, and in 1901 *"it was so excessively abundant in North Essex and on the Suffolk side of the River Stour that I could have taken hundreds of broods had I required them"* (Harwood, 1906). Although a scarce insect for perhaps twenty years after this, Morley (1937) wrote, *"Fortunately we have not shared a diminution in the numbers of this fine species with the south of England"*, and in the years following, the Large Tortoiseshell was recorded every season until the mid-1950's. East Suffolk was the species' British headquarters. There is no simple relationship between abundance in Suffolk and "the great migration years" for other butterfly species; the pattern is rather one of continuous presence, punctuated by periods of unaccountable scarcity. After 1954 the Large Tortoiseshell became very uncommon and this decline was clearly apparent at the time: *"in spite of a thorough search in several known localities, I saw no sign of the Large Tortoiseshell. . . This is strange as the species was quite common in 1954"* (Chipperfield, 1956).

Since the late 1950's there have been one or two reported sightings every couple of years. We are sure that a large proportion of these result from misidentification and it is impossible to know whether the remainder are chance migrants, releases, or evidence of a surviving native population at a very low density. The last sighting was near Woodbridge in 1985 and, because Mr. G. Padfield was able to photograph the butterfly, there can be no question of misidentification.

The Large Tortoiseshell is a butterfly of woodland rides and edges, and tree-lined lanes, but is a strong flyer and used to be a regular visitor to gardens. Butterflies were usually first seen on emergence from hibernation on sunny days in March and April, and these would produce the generation of the year in July and August. The eggs are laid on the terminal twigs of Elm, *Ulmus* spp. and occasionally other species such as Sallow, *Salix* spp. In 1908 *"No less than three hundred specimens were bred from caterpillars that fed on Cherry* (Prunus Cerasus, *L.)"* in a garden at Fornham, near Bury St. Edmunds (Nurse, 1937). The larvae feed communally in a web and in the days when the Large Tortoiseshell was common, these "nests" were easily found.

It has been suggested that the loss of Elm as a result of Dutch Elm Disease makes the "return" of the Large Tortoiseshell unlikely. However, larvae were often found on hedges and scrub growth, of which there is still plenty. Harwood (1906), saw *"one very tall elm hedge on the outskirts of the town [Colchester, Essex] which, for a considerable distance was entirely defoliated"* by larvae. Perhaps the Large Tortoiseshell will one day return, as has its relative the Comma.

Large Tortoiseshell   *(G. Padfield)*

Large Tortoiseshell

(only confirmed records for the two most recent date classes have been plotted)

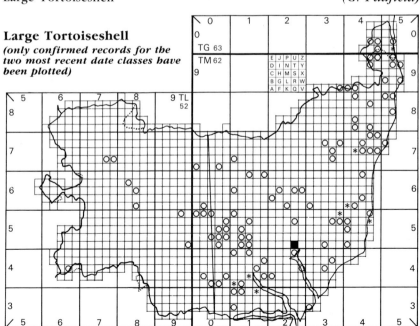

CAMBERWELL BEAUTY *Nymphalis antiopa* L.

The first British specimen of this fine insect was taken in August 1748 in Cool Arbour Lane, Camberwell, which accounts for its common name. It has always been considered a great prize by collectors, and because of this its history is well documented, though somewhat confused by the large number of fraudulent examples and deliberate releases. Beaufoy (1956) recounts that, *"the press in July stated that, at the end of that month about one hundred. . . were released at Greenwich"*. How many less well publicised releases take place? It is also likely that a proportion of specimens seen in this country are "ship assisted", and one was actually, *"seen flying from the hold of a Norwegian timber ship discharging at Felixstowe docks"*, in 1969 [D. A. Young].

There is no evidence to suggest that the Camberwell Beauty breeds in Britain, and naturally occurring specimens are migrants, thought to have come from Northern Europe, and Scandinavia in particular. Interestingly, in 1934 a *"specimen came to rest on a ship's boat at the Corton Lightship, lying 3½ miles off Gunton, on 21 August"* (Morley, 1934), and when disturbed flew strongly westward. It used to be said that genuine British taken specimens always had white rather than ochreous borders to their wings, and indeed the butterfly used to be widely known as the White-bordered. Though a high proportion of those reaching Britain do have white borders, it is not true of all specimens. Williams (1971) considers that the colour of the border is partly connected with the latitude of breeding areas, and is paler in Scandinavia. This helps to explain the high proportion of white-bordered British taken specimens.

Though a few are reported from Britain in most years, very occasionally there is a far larger invasion and these "Camberwell Beauty years" are long remembered in the annals of entomology. The most remarkable year was 1872 when 436 were recorded and, more recently, 1976 takes second place with approaching 300 reports. Suffolk is well placed to receive more than its share of these north European migrants.

Morley (1937a) provides a comprehensive list of the Suffolk records since 1819, and says of 1872; *"A score were netted in as many days in late August to early September"*, and according to George (1965), *"at least forty five of the rare Camberwell Beauty* (Nymphalis antiopa *L.) were reported in our own county"* that year. It is interesting that in 1938, *"A good* Nymphalis antiopa *taken in Suffolk in 1872 realised £1 - 1s"*, at the sale of the W.S. Brocklehurst Collection (Rait-Smith, 1938).

Since 1937 there have been records as follows: **1939** — Lowestoft [R. F. Eley]; **1940** — Saxmundham (Copinger Hill, 1941); **1944** — Somerleyton (Moore, 1944); **1945** — Nayland and Lowestoft (Morley, 1945b); **1946** — Lowestoft (2) and Halesworth (Morley, 1946); **1947** — Leiston, Sizewell, Flatford (3), Beccles, Boyton, Haverhill and Lowestoft (Morley, 1947a), Easton Bavents, Gorleston (Anon, 1947b); **1948** — St. Olaves, 29th March and 11th April [H. E. Jenner]; **1956** — Grundisburgh (Beaufoy, 1956); **1958** — Dunwich (Anon., 1958a); **1968** — Woodbridge and Benacre (Chipperfield, 1969); **1972** — "Suffolk" (Worms, 1973). A list of the **1976** records is given by Chalmers-Hunt (1977 a & b):

Camberwell Beauty   *(H. Mendel)*

Southwold (2), Eye, Saxmundham, Pakefield, Reydon, Henham, Snape, Beccles, Assington, Westleton and Minsmere (possibly 3), and to these may be added Darsham (Chipperfield, 1977), Lowestoft (Anon, 1976) and Kessingland (Worms, 1977). One of the Southwold specimens, seen by P. Tate on 21st August, had bright yellow borders.

A lesser invasion took place in **1984,** one of the years of the Butterfly Survey, and the first report was from Brantham on 15th August. [E. F. Keeble] Its appearance coincided with a large movement of Pied Flycatchers, *Ficedula hypoleuca* (Pallas) and the very same day there was a fall of twenty-five of these passage birds at the nearby Landguard Bird Observatory. The weather patterns also indicated that it was probably a true migrant from Northern Europe. Other Camberwell Beauties were seen in 1984; at Chillesford (TM3951) on 28th August [A. J. Mowles], and nearby (TM 3952), at about the same time (two specimens) [S. Goodrich]. One was seen in an Ipswich garden also in late August [G. C. Raphael], and in September two were reported from Stradbroke [Mrs. O. de Pinto] and another from Monks Eleigh [Dr. P. J. Helliwell]. There were rumours of other sightings, but these unfortunately could not be confirmed.

We were fortunate to see the Brantham specimen, which remained for a second day, attracted to sap seeping from a wound in an Oak. It was very active and would fly away rapidly if disturbed, to return a few minutes later, or sun itself on the bare earth of a nearby track. Camberwell Beauties are also attracted to rotten fruit, especially plums, and in about 1900, E. J. Singleton Smith *"took three or four at a Cossus-tree in marshes below Oulton Church"* (Morley, 1938). The unpleasant smelling sap round wounds in trees attacked by the larvae of the Goat Moth, *Cossus cossus*

L. is known to attract many types of insects. The number of Camberwell Beauties caught in greenhouses in Suffolk over the years is quite extraordinary.

Although the Camberwell Beauty normally appears in late summer or autumn, there are often reports of them in spring following an invasion, and it is presumed these individuals have survived the winter in hibernation. The spring of 1985 was no exception, and the authors were pleased to receive from Mrs. M. Wells of Sibton, the four wings of a Camberwell Beauty, found on the floor of a work room where they had not been the previous day. They were in good condition and it was most likely that the butterfly had been recently killed, perhaps by a mouse.

PEACOCK   *Inachis io* L.

This exotic looking butterfly with four "peacock eyes" is such a familiar garden visitor that further description would be superfluous. The finely figured charcoal-brown under-side makes the Peacock appear near black in flight, and it may easily be mistaken for a Red Admiral.

Widely distributed and generally common throughout most of Britain, but becoming rarer in the north, the Peacock has always been common in Suffolk. It is a wide-ranging, mobile species and must be present in just about every tetrad in the County. It is difficult to decide whether or not the distribution pattern has been influenced significantly by "recorder bias". Certainly urban and suburban areas are on the whole better recorded, but Peacocks do seem to be more numerous in such areas than the open countryside. Sheltered, flowery waysides and woodland edges are other favourite haunts, and the butterflies will spend a long time just basking in the sun, often on a bare patch of earth.

The Peacock is long-lived and overwinters as an adult in the dark corner of an outbuilding or a hollow tree, and assemblages of several dozen or more have been recorded. With wings closed tightly over the abdomen, the underside colour and pattern provide excellent camouflage. Butterflies emerge from hibernation in April, although a few are usually awakened by warm spells in March. It is always a pleasure to see the first Peacocks of the year, which are often attracted to early flowers such as spring Daffodils. Eggs are laid in May, in a dense mass on the under-side of a leaf of Stinging Nettle, *Urtica dioica* L., on which the spiny black larvae feed in a web until ready to pupate.

There is a single generation each year, and after the previous year's butterflies have died, by early June, Peacocks are not seen on the wing again until late July. At this time of the year they spend much of their time taking nectar from the flowers of Field Scabious, Knapweed or Hemp Agrimony, and are especially attracted to Buddleia. They have usually settled into their winter retreats by October. Although not considered to be a regular migrant, Peacocks have been recorded coming in from the sea in Spring on the south coast, and "*in mid-August, 1939, were moving to the south-east past a light vessel about 20 miles off the Suffolk coast*" (Williams, 1971).

Peacock   *(R. Beecroft)*

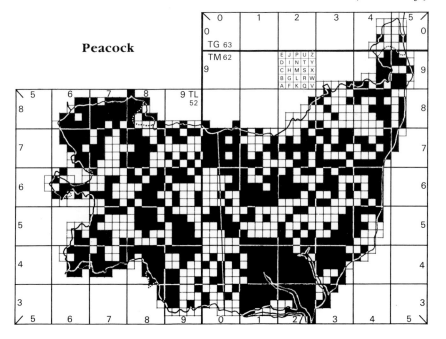

COMMA *Polygonia c-album* L.

The unusual and irregular wing outline readily distinguishes the Comma from all other British butterflies, and the white "comma" mark on the under-side of the hind wings gives the species its name. This mark is somewhat variable in shape, and is occasionally closed to form a circle.

The Comma has a very interesting history in both Suffolk and the rest of Britain. In Suffolk it was considered a great rarity throughout the 19th century, and until the mid-1930's. Bloomfield (1890) considered it *"Very rare"*, which was hardly surprising as he knew of only three of the very few reports of the butterfly in the County up to that time. Though widespread across much of southern England in the first half of the last century, the Comma became very scarce, and by the turn of the century was confined to Gloucestershire, Herefordshire and Monmouthshire. The two Suffolk records from this period of low ebb are of considerable interest. Morley (1937a) recorded, *"One flying at Ipswich near the Gipping on 19th September 1892"* and *"one in Thorndon rectory garden in 1912"*.

It was during the second decade of this century that the Comma began to spread from its stronghold, though it was not until 1935/6 that it was reported from Suffolk. Its recurrence in Suffolk was no gradual spread from west to east; indeed, one of the early reports was from Felixstowe (French, 1936). These early reports were treated with scepticism (Morley, 1941), and it was not until 1937, when Commas were seen all across Suffolk (Morley, 1937b), that doubt was dispelled. Even today the spread of the species, beyond its previously recorded range, is as much of a mystery as was the cause of its decline.

The Comma is a strong flyer and, though essentially a woodland butterfly, may appear just about anywhere in the County, as the map indicates. It is a frequent visitor to gardens, especially in the late summer when attracted by the flowers of Buddleia, Mint and Michaelmas Daisies, and may be seen in even the most urban areas. However, it is most at home along woodland rides and edges, and here the larvae may be found on either Stinging Nettle, *Urtica dioica* L. or Elm, *Ulmus* spp. In Suffolk, larvae have also been found on Hop, *Humulus lupulus* L., another of its known foodplants.

This is one of the earliest species to appear in the year, and a few are usually brought out of hibernation by warm sunny days in March. These early butterflies produce the first generation in June and July, which in turn produce a second flight from August onwards. First generation Commas are more brightly orange, with paler under-sides and less deeply indented wings, and have been called the form *hutchinsoni*. They may easily be mistaken for one of the larger fritillaries when in flight, and are probably responsible for a large proportion of "Fritillary sp." reports during the Survey.

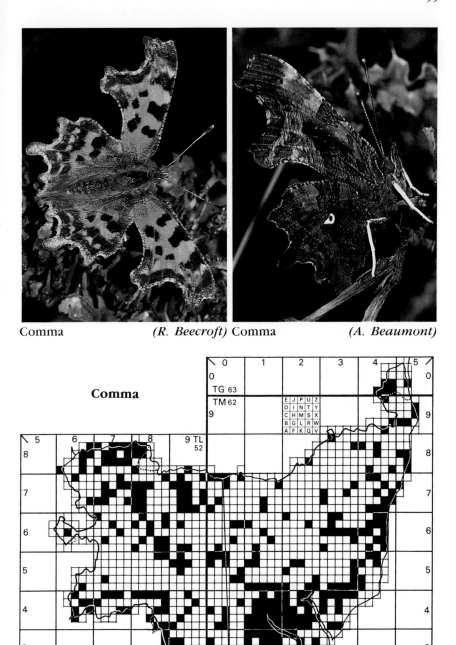

Comma   *(R. Beecroft)* Comma   *(A. Beaumont)*

SMALL PEARL-BORDERED FRITILLARY *Boloria selene* D. & S.

This species and the next, the Pearl-bordered Fritillary, are easily confused, but sadly this confusion will not be a problem in Suffolk as both have been lost. The Small Pearl-bordered Fritillary is most reliably separated by the many more silver markings on the under-side of its hind wings.

In Britain the Small Pearl-bordered Fritillary is found from the north of Scotland to the south coast, but its range has contracted westwards during this century. It disappeared from Suffolk in the late 1950's or early 1960's. It was said to be common in Suffolk in the last century, and this is a possible reason for there being so few localised records, but more likely it was common in the south-east, but unknown over much of the County. According to Paget (1834) it was found in the north-east at *"Lound wood and heath; rare; May and June "*, but the early date and the fact that the then commoner Pearl-bordered Fritillary does not appear in his list, suggest he may have confused the two species. It merited no more comment than *"Common"* by Greene (1857), Stainton (1857) had information that is was common about Stowmarket, and Newman (1870-71) gives as localities; *"Coomb, Bentley etc.* — H. H. Crewe; *Brandeston and Playford* — Joseph Greene; *Sudbury* — W. D. King"*. Bloomfield (1890) remarked that it was *"common round Ipswich but. . . scarcely recorded elsewhere"* and, other than repeating Paget, listed as localities only *"Ipswich, Bentley etc."*

In 1937 Morley wrote that it *"Still continues to be quite frequent in Bentley Woods"*, undoubtedly the stronghold of the species, and there are few records from elsewhere this century. It had gone from here too by 1959 (Worms, 1979), but interestingly for that same year the national Biological Records Centre has a record for Assington Thicks (C. R. Heseltine).

In Suffolk the Small Pearl-bordered Fritillary was a species of damper woodlands and associated areas of bog where the larval food-plant, Common Wood Violet, *Viola riviniana* Rchb., was plentiful. It was usually on the wing in June and July, somewhat later than the Pearl-bordered Fritillary, but has been recorded in May, and in 1942 had finished as early as the 5th July (Morley, 1942).

PEARL-BORDERED FRITILLARY *Boloria euphrosyne* L.

This species is easily confused with the superficially very similar Small Pearl-bordered Fritillary, and in Britain the range of both species has contracted westward. It is much less common in the north than the Small Pearl-bordered Fritillary, more local in distribution throughout its range, and declining.

In Suffolk the Pearl-bordered Fritillary was certainly more common and widespread than the Small Pearl-bordered, and no doubt for this reason there are so few localised records. Greene (1857) considered it

Pearl-bordered Fritillary   *(P. Summers)*

"*Common*", and the same year "*several dozen*" were taken in Fakenham Wood in early June (Tillett, 1857), and Stainton (1857) said it was to be found commonly about Stowmarket. Hele (1870) found it "*Abundant in Sudbourne Woods*" and according to Bloomfield (1890) it was "*Locally common*" and found at "*Needham and many localities near Ipswich; also Monk Park Wood [Bradfield Woods] A. H. W. [A. H. Wrattislaw]*". It was well known from Raydon Wood where it lasted until at least 1945 (Beaufoy, 1970), and at the Ipswich Museum is a series of four taken there in the last week of May in 1898, by J. H. Hocking. It was still found at "*Fakenham Wood in 1933 (Kirby)*" (Morley, 1937a), and at Bradfield Woods "*one worn* Euphrosyne *was seen in Felsham Wood on 1 June*" in 1943 by F. G. Barcock (Vinter, 1943). Since that time it has been seen only at Home Wood, Hitcham on 16th May 1948 [A. L. Bull], and in its best known locality, the Bentley/Belstead woods to the south of Ipswich. Describing a visit to this area in 1958 Aston (1959) wrote; "*On May 27th, I went to Bentley Woods... In brilliant noon sunshine it was pleasing to see a flight of the fine Large Pearl-bordered Fritillary* (Argynnis euphrosyne, *L.). They fluttered near the ground in dozens, attending the flowers of bugle*". The Pearl-bordered Fritillary was seen nearby at Belstead the following year (Beaufoy, 1970), but has not been recorded in Suffolk since.

The Pearl-bordered Fritillary was a woodland butterfly in Suffolk, usually found about clearings and woodland edges in May or June, and overlapping in season with the previous species. The larvae of both fed on Common Wood Violet, *Viola riviniana* Rchb., and it is interesting that they both became extinct in Suffolk in the late 1950's.

WEAVER'S FRITILLARY   *Boloria dia* L.

This widely distributed European species, resembling the Pearl-bordered Fritillary, has been recorded from Britain on several occasions, though does not have an accepted place on the British list. No doubt some of the records are fraudulent, or result from misidentification or accidental introduction, but others are difficult to explain away.

A male Weaver's Fritillary was taken by E. W. Platten, who wrote on 9th July 1942:

> *"Having a surplus of common Butterflies and Moths in 1900 I set them out geometrically in a sealed glass case where they remained till 1941, when the Fritillaries were still unfaded. Then I broke open the case and noticed one* A. selene *a good deal smaller than is typical, with curious underside; this I showed, and have now presented, to our Hon. Secretary who ascertains it to be* Argynnis Dia, L. *Its origin is given by my old diary: on '16 May 1899. Took large numbers of* Euphrosyne *at Bentley Woods near Ipswich and, in an adjacent marsh, one very small specimen of that species or an early* Selene' *"* (Vinter, 1942a).

The specimen still stands in the collection of the then Hon. Secretary, Claude Morley, at the Ipswich Museum. There is no doubt that it is a Weaver's Fritillary.

QUEEN OF SPAIN FRITILLARY   *Argynnis lathonia* L.

A scarce migrant to Britain, though widespread on the Continent and resident *"along the North Sea coast"* in Holland (Williams, 1971). The appearance of the Queen of Spain in Britain is unpredictable, and the species has not been recorded breeding here *"unless we accept the record in* The Zoologist *for 1862, stating that a larva was found suspended for pupation on a Hazel Branch near Sudbury, Suffolk"* (Frohawk, 1934a). There is, however, good indirect evidence that the species does, occasionally, successfully produce a generation in this country. There are one or two sightings in Britain most years, usually in the south-east, and very occasionally many more are seen. In 1945, the best year for the species this century, no less than 37 were reported.

Jermyn (1824) recorded the Queen of Spain *"On the Dandelion in dry pastures by a wood in Stoke by Nayland"*, and in Morley's annotated 1827 edition had been inserted *"middle of September near Ipswich 1826"*. At some time before 1857, seven were *"taken in a clover field near Ipswich, by Mr. Garrod, of that town"* (Greene, 1857). Newman (1870-71) lists the records known to him, some already published and including those for the exceptional year of 1868:

> *"One specimen on the 3rd Sept., at Lavenham... on the blossom of a dandelion... — W. Gaze;... by Captain Russell on two occasions, in August, 1859; in the first instance five specimens in the second two... at Lavenham; the specimens*

were shown to the late Professor Henslow — Report of Entomological Society, *Feb. 3, 1862; one in clover-field, near Ipswich, August, 1868* — Garrett Garrett; *one at Stowmarket in August 1868* — W Baker; *one in a clover-field at Hazelwood, near Aldeburgh, on the 3rd September, 1868* — N. Fenwick Hele."

As well as the one taken at Aldeburgh by Hele on 3rd September, *"Another specimen was taken a few days later, near the church"* and *"Five examples have at different times occurred in the immediate neighbourhood"* (Hele, 1870). Newman (1870-71) also records *"one at Bury-St.-Edmunds* — A. H. Wrattislaw", but wrongly assigns this to Essex. This is no doubt the same locality as the *"Icklingham"* referred to by Wrattislaw (1870), who had previously taken an example *"At Aldeburgh, in July "* 1865 (Wrattislaw, 1865). A further specimen was taken at Ipswich in 1871 (Knaggs, 1872) and the following year, the best ever nationally for the species, another two at Ipswich *"flying over the Phlox Drumondii"* (Long, 1872), one at Aldeburgh on the 18th September by A. E. Garrod (Hunt, 1872), and *"On July 26th, 1872, a dead specimen of this butterfly was found on the shore at Felixstowe, which no doubt was an emigrant"* (Frohawk, 1934a). After that date until the end of the century there were *"five specimens at Aldeburgh in August 1886"* (T. and J. Brown) according to Bloomfield (1890), who also gives Bradwell as a locality for the species. Finally, H. Calver took one *"in early July 1888 near the north boundary of Belstead"* (Platten, 1941a) the last of the century.

Surprisingly, the very last Suffolk Queen of Spain Fritillary was seen at Battisford in August, 1900 (Baker, 1900), and since then there has not been a single confirmed report. The 1975 Southwold Queen of Spain (Anon, 1975) has not been accepted.

NIOBE FRITILLARY *Argynnis niobe* L.

British records of this Continental species resembling the High Brown Fritillary are few, and all would seem to be associated with some degree of doubt. In this respect the Suffolk Niobe Fritillary is no exception.

A summary of its history is provided by its "captor" T. N. Waller (1935):

"I feel that evidence, especially the most fortunate isolation of my Welsh captures strongly points to Monks-park Wood [Bradfield St. Clare] as the locality of origin of our Argynnis Niobe, L. But the period of its capture is so far back in the dim past and somewhat confused in early boyhood's memories that I cannot definitely state that I myself took the specimen".

The identity of this specimen, now in the Morley Collection at the Ipswich Museum, is not in question. It is a male of the commoner form of the the species (f. *eris* Meigen) as confirmed by C. G. Barrett (Cottam, 1900). However, *"boyhood's memories"* cannot be relied upon, especially where so unlikely a species is concerned.

HIGH BROWN FRITILLARY *Argynnis adippe* D. & S.

One of three large species of fritillary found in Britain, and liable to be confused with the other two unless a good view of the under-side is obtained. The series of rust-red spots with silver centres, just inside the silver spots around the margin of the hind wings, readily identifies the High Brown Fritillary.

Though widely distributed in England and Wales, as far north as Cumberland, and found in most of the larger woods until the 1950's, this species has declined westwards and is now one of the scarcer British butterflies.

The High Brown Fritillary used to be widespread and locally common in Suffolk woodlands. Jermyn (1827) gave as localities *"Old Hall, Hull and Dodnash Woods, and Bentley, Suffolk"*, and because Bree considered the species *"Common"* (Greene, 1857), a list of localities was thought unnecessary. According to Bloomfield (1890) the High Brown was *"Very local Bentley, Belstead, Wherstead, etc., all near Ipswich"* and Morley (1937a) had only a few additional localities. However, the renewed interest in the butterflies of Suffolk, following the publication of Morley's *"Lepidoptera of Suffolk"*, produced a different picture. Throughout the 1940's and early 1950's the High Brown Fritillary was to be found widely in Suffolk, and was recorded from as far afield as Staverton Park (Beaufoy, 1970), Redgrave Fen (Vinter, 1946), Saxham (Tickner, 1941), St. Olaves [H. E. Jenner] and Henham [W. S. George]. The decline of the species in the late 1950's was rapid and the last specimens were seen in Suffolk in 1959, by S. Beaufoy (Beaufoy, 1970) at Belstead and H. E. Chipperfield in the Stowmarket area (Anon, 1959).

The High Brown Fritillary was a woodland species in Suffolk, equally at home amongst the Oaks of Staverton and Iken as the coppice of south Suffolk or the heathland scrub at Knettishall. The larvae feed on various species of Violet, *Viola* spp. and produce a single generation of adults on the wing between late June and early August. They are strong flyers and attracted to various nectar flowers, especially Thistles.

High Brown Fritillary   *(B. Sawford)*

High Brown Fritillary

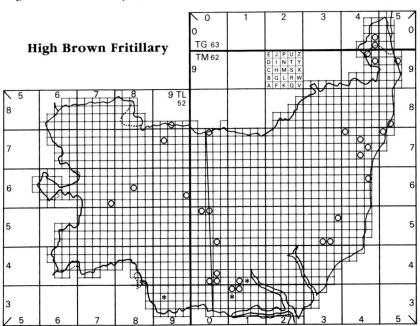

DARK GREEN FRITILLARY *Argynnis aglaja* L.

Found locally throughout most of Britain, the Dark Green Fritillary is easily confused with the very similar High Brown, and is best known from that species by the absence of the silver-pupilled, red spots on the under-side of the hind wings. This fritillary has always been uncommon in Suffolk, and the majority of reports refer to single specimens. Jermyn (1827) knew of the species to the east of Ipswich at *"Nacton Heath and Bixley Decoy"* and *"Curtis, in his 'British Entomology', 1830, figures a very dark variety of* Aglaia *which he informs us were taken by Mr. John Seaman, in the parish of Nacton, near Ipswich, the 7th of July, 1827"* (Dale, 1890). About the same time it was said to be common on Lound Heath in the north-east of the County (Paget, 1834), and although Bree had *"no certain information"* that the Dark Green Fritillary was found in Suffolk (Greene, 1857), Newman (1870-71) had records from *"Bentley, Stowmarket —* H. H. Crewe [and] *Sudbury —* John Grubb". *"But one example has come under notice"* wrote Hele (1870) *"from the neighbourhood of Snape, in 1868"*, and Bloomfield (1890) who considered the species to be *"Rare"* added Tuddenham, West Suffolk (A. H. Wrattislaw and T. & J. Brown), and Bentley (G. Garrett) where it was rediscovered in 1942 *"on the outskirts of Bentley Woods where I took some on 5 July"* (Vinter, 1942b).

Morley (1937a) knew of a single additional record, *"Copdock on 3 July 1895 (Hkg)* [J. H. Hocking]" and thought it was *"Probably extinct"*, though as is often the case after such a declaration, this was soon to be proved wrong. In the 1940's and early 50's it was not only recorded from Bentley but also: Barking Woods (Platten, 1941b), Westleton (Vinter, 1944), Blaxhall Heath [C. Garrett-Jones], Blythburgh (Vinter, 1950), Barton Mills [A. E. Aston] and Redgrave Fen [A. L. Bull]. We have not accepted the very few post-1955 records known to us.

Although the Dark Green Fritillary has been recorded from Suffolk woodlands, it is more a species of open ground and especially heathland. It flies powerfully and quickly, and can be very difficult to identify with certainty when not prepared to settle. Male Oak Eggars, *Lasiocampa quercus* L. and Fox Moths, *Macrothylacia rubi* L. fly by day over Suffolk's heathland, and have in flight been mistaken for the Dark Green Fritillary. The larvae feed on various species of Violet, *Viola* spp. and the single generation of adults is usually on the wing from early July to the middle of August.

SILVER-WASHED FRITILLARY *Argynnis paphia* L.

A large, showy butterfly more strikingly spotted than the previous two species, and with the veins of the central area of the fore wings picked out with black in the males. The under-sides of the hind wings are most attractively marbled with silver and green, and give the species its name. In some areas a proportion of the females have the orange-brown of the upper-side replaced by grey-green, and this form *valezina,* best known

Dark Green Fritillary   *(B. J. Wingrove)*

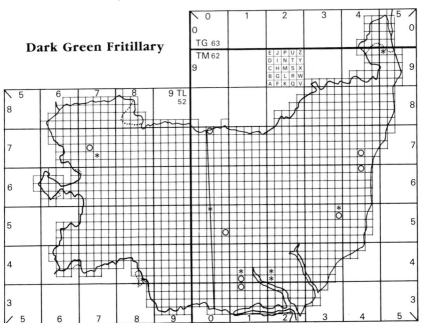

Dark Green Fritillary

from the New Forest, has been reported from Suffolk, but not before New Forest stock had been released here.

Though still found widely in southern and especially western Britain, as far north as North Wales, the Silver-washed Fritillary is becoming more local and contracting in range to the south and the west. Jermyn (1827) knew of the species from "*Old Hall, Hull and Dodnash Woods and Bentley*" to the south of Ipswich, and in north-east Suffolk, Paget (1834) writes of "*a single specimen taken at Bradwell*". Greene (1857) has no more to say of the species than "*Common*", and Brandon is given as a locality by Miller and Skertchley (1878). Bloomfield (1890) probably more accurately assessed the status as "*Common about Ipswich, but rare elsewhere*" adding "*Saxham, Needham Market and Redisham*" to the known localities. Morley (1937a) wrote that the Silver-washed Fritillary was "*Numerous in Assington Woods (Sudbury Journal 1838; Ransom 1898)*" and took the species himself at Bentley Woods in 1893 and 1895. There was not a single Suffolk record between 1910 and 1937, leading Morley (1937a) to proclaim that it was "*Probably extinct*" in Suffolk.

"*The dearth, or even possible loss of the beautiful* Argynnis Paphia *of recent years throughout Suffolk and its ubiquity in the New Forest induced me to take eggs from a batch of about twenty specimens caught in the latter during August 1939 and lay them down in the Barking Woods near Needham Market.*"
(Burton, 1940).

The introduction was "successful" and over the following years the Silver-washed Fritillary was often seen, not only at the original site but in woodlands throughout the area [G. J. Burton]. Was the species extinct in Suffolk at that time? Definitely not. It was in fact recorded from "*Badley on 13 and 14 July*" 1938 by E. W. Platten and J. Goddard (Morley, 1938), and from "*near Ipswich railway station on 2 Sept.*" 1939, by G. J. Burton (Vinter, 1939). E. W. Platten assured H. E. Chipperfield that the Silver-washed Fritillary was actually in the Barking Woods at the time of the introduction [H. E. Chipperfield].

During the 1940's and 50's the species seems to have become widespread in Suffolk again. How much this was due to the introduction to the Barking Woods we shall never know, but it is unlikely that even such a mobile species as the Silver-washed Fritillary could have reached St. Olaves [H. E. Jenner] by 1946, or Saxham, nr. Bury St. Edmunds by 1941 (Tickner, 1941). It is indeed unfortunate that this introduction seems to have coincided with a genuine resurgence. By the late 1950's the species was extremely scarce again and reports since that time have not been confirmed.

The Silver-washed Fritillary is on the wing in suitable woodlands between late June and the middle of August, depending on the season, and the butterflies are particularly attracted to Thistles and Bramble flowers. The eggs are laid not on the foodplant Violet, *Viola* spp., but on the bark or lichen growth of nearby trees. However, the only published account of egg laying in Suffolk describes the eggs "*lain on extreme tips of growing Moss. . . at the base of an Ash-tree, some feet from the ground and near Violets*" (Platten, 1941b).

Silver-washed Fritillary ♀   *(B. Sawford)*

Silver-washed Fritillary

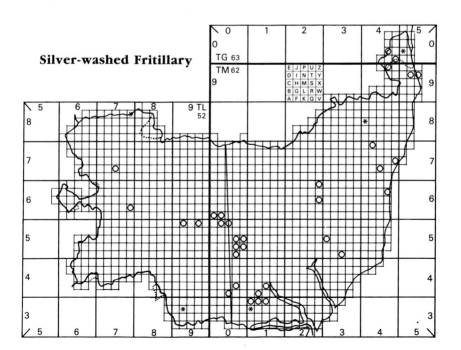

MARSH FRITILLARY *Eurodryas aurinia* Rott.

Colonies of the Marsh Fritillary occur in a variety of habitats in Britain, marshy meadows, calcareous grassland, woodland glades and moorland, the common factor being the presence of the larval foodplant, Devil's-bit Scabious, *Succisa pratensis* Moench. Though once found locally over much of Britain, the butterfly's decline westward in England started well before the end of the last century (Luckens, 1978) and was particularly severe in the 1940's and 50's (Heath, Pollard and Thomas, 1984). There are only 19th and very early 20th century records from Suffolk.

Jermyn (1827) recorded the butterfly (then known as the Greasy Fritillary) from *"Eriswell and Mildenhall"* and Bree reported that it was taken *"by Mr. Arthur Simpson, close to my grounds at Stowmarket, in May, 1857"* (Greene, 1857). Garness (1857) wrote that it was found, *"in the greatest abundance in some marshes close to Bungay"* by his father *"a few years since"*, but they never saw one there later, and Newman (1870-71) adds to these localities, *"Brandeston and Playford* — Joseph Greene *[and] Haverhill* — W Gaze". W. M. Crowfoot's record for *"Near Beccles"* (Bloomfield, 1890) is no doubt the same as his *"Near Aldeby, but confined to a few marshes"* (Newman, 1870-71) and should probably be assigned to Norfolk.

Suffolk's most persistent colony was to be found in the Tuddenham Fen area of West Suffolk (Wrattislaw, 1870), and it occurred here annually until at least 1904, on the marshy meadow beside the mill in Tuddenham Village, according to Sparke, *"who took two and saw more. . . in May 1898"*, but none were to be found in 1929 (Morley, 1937). A further thorough search of the area in 1947 likewise proved negative (Vinter, 1947).

GLANVILLE FRITILLARY *Melitaea cinxia* L.

A species on the very edge of its range in southern Britain, and now confined to the Isle of Wight. The Glanville Fritillary is known to have occurred along the Kentish coast in the mid-nineteenth century and there are scattered records from inland dating back to the eighteenth century.

Stainton (1857) recorded the Glanville Fritillary from Stowmarket, Suffolk, and in spite of the fact that the record was withdrawn (Greene, 1857), it has persisted in the literature. There are no genuine records of the Glanville Fritillary from Suffolk.

HEATH FRITILLARY *Mellicta athalia* Rott.

A rare and declining species in Britain, now restricted to Kent and the south-west where very few colonies remain. The Heath Fritillary has been reintroduced to other areas in an attempt to safeguard its future, but must still be considered an endangered species. An interesting review of some of the early reintroductions is provided by Luckens (1980).

Marsh Fritillary   *(B. Sawford)*

In Suffolk this butterfly seems to have been confined to the south-east, and became extinct in the 19th century. It was recorded from *"Woods to the south of Ipswich"* in 1836 (Delta, 1837), and according to C. R. Bree, *"Mr King, the dealer, once showed me a series of this insect, which he stated he had taken near Ipswich"* (Greene, 1857). Heath Fritillaries have also been recorded from Stowmarket (Stainton, 1857), but almost certainly in error, and *"Brandeston and Playford* — Joseph Greene" (Newman, 1870-71).

Morley (1937a) wrote:

> *"The last seem to have been captured at Bentley by Mr. Coleman (Garrett); an old Ipswich collector tells me he used to take it at Old Hall Wood near Bentley, where other collectors used also to take it, thirty years ago (Henry Miller, 1890). Now extinct probably through over-collecting."*

It is likely that over-collecting did play a part in the demise of the Heath Fritillary, which is especially susceptible as it tends to form small colonies and has poor powers of dispersal. *"Pheasants are known to be particularly fond of the early stages"* (Howarth, 1973), and this may have been a contributory factor.

SPECKLED WOOD   *Pararge aegeria* L.

This attractive dark-brown, yellow-spotted butterfly is unlikely to be confused with any other if seen at rest. However, a Wall or Meadow Brown flying through woodland in dappled sunlight can look very similar. The Speckled Wood is widely distributed in southern England, the midland counties, Wales and parts of Scotland, and is probably still extending its range following a major contraction towards the end of the last century.

In Suffolk Jermyn (1827) recorded the Speckled Wood from "*Woods near Baylham Hall, and in the Lanes near the Race Ground, Ipswich*", and in the north-east it was common at Lound Wood (Paget, 1834). It seems to have been widespread and generally common in the County throughout much of the 19th century, and was even said to be "*Very abundant*" (Green, 1857). Bloomfield (1890) wrote that it was "*Generally common*", but records suggest that by then the Speckled Wood had already become extremely scarce. From the 1890's until its return to Suffolk in the 1960's, the only authentic record seems to be of "*two examples in the garden of Koolunga House in Gorleston during 1918*" (Morley, 1932b), which may have been introductions or escapes (Morley, 1937a).

"*In 1960 it was found to be flourishing at Great Hockham [Norfolk] in afforested Breckland*" (Ellis, 1984), and in 1964 the first Suffolk specimens from near Thetford were shown at the annual conversazione of the South London Entomological Society (Aston, 1966). Records followed from areas of conifer plantation in north-west Suffolk, and in 1969 it was seen in the King's Forest (Beaufoy, 1970). Since that time the Speckled Wood has spread through the extensive conifer plantations of Breckland Suffolk and into other habitats such as naturally re-generating heathland scrub and riverside poplar plantations. It has been slow to penetrate Suffolk's coppice woodlands, although some have been seen in the Bradfield Woods near Felsham, and there are reports from a few other outlying areas. Records from the coastal belt have yet to be confirmed, but it seems likely that colonisation of the extensive conifer plantations in that area will take place.

The Speckled Wood is a butterfly of tracks, rides, firebreaks and woodland edges in Suffolk. It seems to prefer sheltered areas where the canopy produces a pattern of light and shade on the vegetation beneath. The butterflies feed on honeydew, but will also visit flowers such as Ragwort. Males defend territories from sunny spots amongst the shade.

The larvae of the Speckled Wood feed on various grasses, and Common Couch, *Agropyron repens* (L.) Beauv. and Cock's-foot *Dactylis glomerata* L., both very common in Suffolk, are said to be preferred. Butterflies may be seen on the wing between April and October and there is now convincing evidence to support the old idea that there are two generations a year, each in two parts. Overwintering pupae hatch in the early spring. Overwintering larvae pupate in the spring and produce butterflies from June to mid-July. In favourable seasons both parts of this first emergence produce a second generation (Robertson, 1980).

Speckled Wood   *(J. A. Foster)*

Speckled Wood

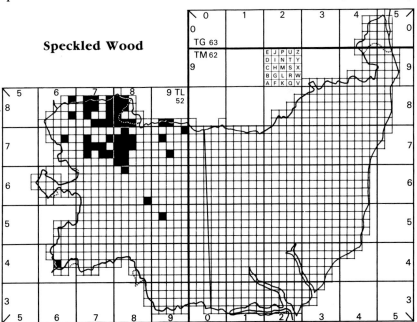

WALL   *Lasiommata megera* L.

It is not difficult to see why this bright orange-brown butterfly with dark markings is sometimes mistaken for one of the smaller fritillaries. The white-pupilled eye-spots visible on both upper and under-sides will, however, readily identify the Wall.

It is generally distributed in Britain as far north as southern Scotland, but becomes more local in the north. *"Abundant"*, *"common"* and *"widespread"* are terms that have in the past been employed to describe the status of the Wall in Suffolk, and Morley (1937a) wrote that it was *"still just as 'very abundant' as it was in 1857"*, from one end of the County to the other. Today the range is more restricted and it is very local in the intensive arable areas. Surprisingly, the Wall is also local in the Breckland, and is found more commonly on the nearby fen soils.

The first butterflies of the year normally appear from the middle of May, and this first brood is on the wing until the end of June, followed by a second brood in late July and August. Second brood butterflies are usually much more plentiful, and in favourable seasons there is a small third emergence in late September. The Wall is most frequently seen in areas of poor soils where the vegetation is sparse, leaving areas of bare ground. Butterflies will bask in the sun on the warm earth or patrol back and forth over some chosen piece of ground. Chalk and gravel pits, crumbling coastal cliffs, heathland tracks, river banks and woodland edges all provide suitable habitats. In the fenland of north-west Suffolk artificial sub-soil banks and dykes are especially favoured.

Communal roosting has been observed in Suffolk on several occasions; *"on one small post twenty-one sleeping* Parage Megaera *were counted"* (Webster, 1941) and *"no less than seven specimens almost touching"* were found beneath the corner of a cap-stone on a wooden post (Morley, 1943). The larvae feed on various grass species, including Cock's-foot, *Dactylis glomerata* L., Wood False Brome, *Brachypodium sylvaticum* (Huds.) Beauv. and Yorkshire Fog, *Holcus lanatus* L.

*MOUNTAIN RINGLET   *Erebia epiphron* Knoch

*SCOTCH ARGUS   *Erebia aethiops* Esp.

MARBLED WHITE   *Melanargia galathea* L.

One of the "browns" in spite of its name, the Marbled White is a grassland butterfly of uncultivated hillsides, open woodland and coastal cliffs. It is most frequent in chalk and limestone areas in the south-west and south midlands, and has not occurred naturally in Suffolk for over a hundred years. Blackie (1951) comments on the species' *"unexplained aversion for East Anglia."* It used to be found on the chalk in the Gipping Valley, at *"Little Blakenham Chalk Pits"* (Jermyn, 1827) and according to C.

Wall ♀   *(A. Beaumont)*

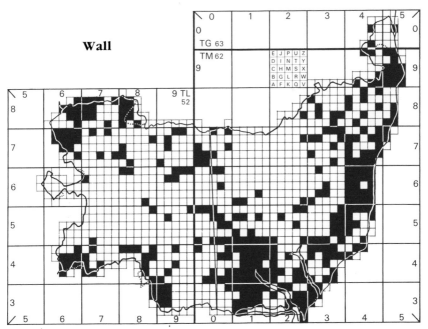

R. Bree it was *"reported to have been taken on the chalk hills about Coddenham a few years ago"* (Greene, 1857). The species was also known to H. Lingwood at *"Needham before 1850"* (Bloomfield, 1890). Outside this chalk area the Marbled White is recorded from *"Beccles — C. G. Barrett"* by Newman (1870-71) but it is quite likely that this report refers to a Norfolk site.

It is rumoured that an attempt was made to introduce the Marbled White to a site on the chalk near Newmarket in the late 1970's or early 1980's, but precise details have not been forthcoming. A specimen in the King's Forest in 1979 [R. P. Ryan] must also have been introduced.

GRAYLING *Hipparchia semele* L.

An attractive brown butterfly with straw-yellow and orange marks forming a band across the wings. The upper-side can only be seen in flight as the wings are shut tightly immediately the butterfly settles. The patterning of the under-side hind wings provides perfect camouflage and the Grayling literally dissolves into the background as soon as the eyed fore wings are tucked beneath them. As if this was not good enough they will tilt sideways into the sun and so cast the minimum shadow. However, this behaviour may be more to do with the regulation of body temperature than camouflage (Findlay *et al.*, 1983).

A grassland species, the Grayling is widespread on heathlands in the South of England and is found around much of the British coast. It was regarded as *"Not uncommon"* in Suffolk by Greene (1857) and *"Common on heaths and sandy lands"* (Bloomfield, 1890). By the late 1930's it was still frequent on the Sandlings and *"Abundant all over the Breck District"* (Morley, 1937a). The distribution today closely reflects the distribution of heathland in Suffolk: the Sandlings, Breckland, scattered northern commons and southern heath remnants. Outside these areas Graylings are plentiful along the coast on cliffs, denes and fixed shingle, and still may be found on the chalk grassland in the west and in a few chalk pits.

Graylings prefer sparse grassland on poor soils with areas of bare ground, and well established colonies may be found in both exposed coastal areas and sheltered tracks and firebreaks in the conifer forests. Individual butterflies often wander away from their usual haunts, especially later in the season, and are regularly seen in Ipswich gardens. There is a single generation each year, and in Suffolk butterflies are usually on the wing from the second week of July until early September, or sometimes later, depending on the weather.

Graylings are most often seen when flushed from the ground along a track, when they will fly off erratically for a short distance and then settle again on bare earth, natural litter or low on a tree trunk. They occasionally visit the flowers of Thistles or Heathers, and in gardens are attracted to Buddleia. The larvae feed on a wide variety of grasses and, unlike any other British butterfly, pupate in a moth-like subterranean cocoon.

Grayling

(S. Beaufoy)

Grayling

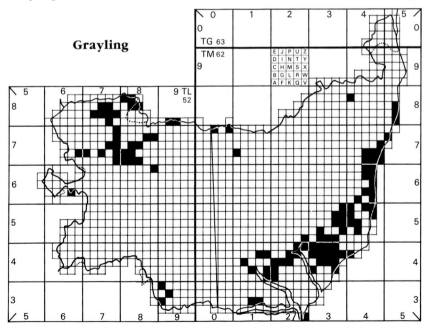

GATEKEEPER *Pyronia tithonus* L.

Equally well known as the Hedge Brown, this species may be identified by the broad orange-brown patch on each wing and the large black, double-pupilled eye-spot towards the apex of the fore wings. The males are smaller with a dark oblique band across the orange area of the fore wings.

The Gatekeeper is distributed throughout England, becoming more local north of the midlands. Morley (1937a) well summarized its status in Suffolk when he wrote that it had been ubiquitous in the County since at least 1827. It is one of Suffolk's most common and widespread species and must be present in every tetrad. Colonies may be found in all sorts of habitats: hedgerows, scrubby field edges, woodland edges and rides, lane sides and roadside verges. It swarms in favoured localities and Mr. A. J. R. Paine estimated that there were 650 around two bramble bushes at Landguard in August 1977 (Chipperfield, 1978). The Gatekeeper was until recently one of the few species little affected by many of the modern farming practices, but now with the removal of many hedgerows it is becoming much more local on Suffolk's "prairies".

It is single brooded and on the wing even in dull weather for the greater part of July and August. The eggs are laid on various grasses, and Annual Meadow-grass, *Poa annua* L., Cocksfoot, *Dactylis glomerata* L. and Bents, *Agrostis* spp. have been recorded as larval foodplants.

MEADOW BROWN *Maniola jurtina* L.

The female is sometimes confused with the smaller Gatekeeper, but in the Meadow Brown the area of orange on each fore wing is smaller and paler, the eye-spots usually single-pupilled, and there are no orange patches on the hind wings. The under-side will readily separate the darker males from Ringlets.

Found throughout the British Isles, the Meadow Brown is probably our most abundant indigenous butterfly. It has been common in Suffolk since recording began, and during the Survey was recorded from more tetrads than any other species. It is a grassland butterfly and may be found on any grassy areas from the depths of the countryside to the centre of towns. Field and woodland edges, roadside verges, heaths, commons, coastal cliffs and riverbanks all support large populations, and though absent from well mown parks and recreation areas, the species is quick to colonise derelict land in urban areas.

The slow flapping flight of the Meadow Brown is characteristic, and butterflies are on the wing even in dull weather. This is one of the reasons they are so well recorded. Knapweeds and Brambles are favourite nectar flowers of the waysides, but Buddleia in village gardens is also an attraction. The larvae feed on grasses, often a Meadow-grass, *Poa* spp., and in Suffolk the butterflies are on the wing from the middle of June until September. It is not definitely known whether there are two generations or a single protracted emergence each year.

Gatekeeper or Hedge Brown ♀
(R. Beecroft)

Meadow Brown ♀   *(S. Beaufoy)*

Gatekeeper or Hedge Brown

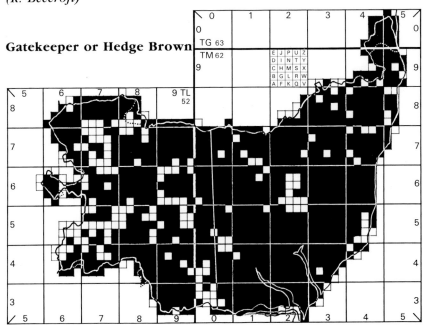

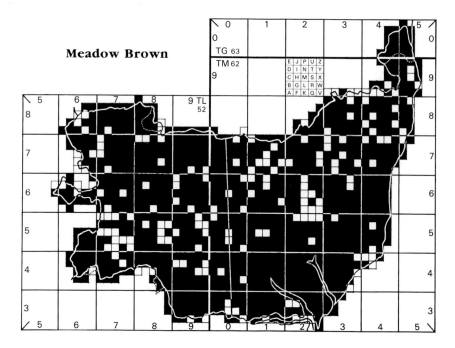

Meadow Brown

SMALL HEATH *Coenonympha pamphilus* L.

This attractive little butterfly with pale orange-brown upper-side and variable grey-brown wing borders is the smallest of the "browns". It flies close to the ground, settling with wings closed, and when at rest lowers the fore wings with their single eye-spots, beneath the cryptic hind wings.

The Small Heath is one of the most widely distributed British butterflies, and remains one of the commoner species in Suffolk. In the middle of the last century it was *"Very common"* (Greene, 1857), as it was eighty years later when Morley (1937a) wrote that it was found *"everywhere throughout the County."* Today it is somewhat more local away from the coast, Sandlings and Breckland heaths; no doubt due to loss of grassland habitat.

Sparse or well grazed grassland, especially on the poorer soils of heathland and coast, provide habitat for the largest populations, but most areas of grassland will support at least small colonies. Forest rides, roadside verges, railway banks and cuttings, coastal shingle, pits, quarries and even derelict land in urban areas are all suitable habitats. The Small Heath is on the wing from the middle of May until September, or even later if good weather holds. The larvae feed on species of grass, and Fescues, *Festuca* spp. and Meadow-grasses, *Poa* spp. are thought to be preferred.

*LARGE HEATH *Coenonympha tullia* Müll.

Small Heath   *(R. Beecroft)*

Small Heath

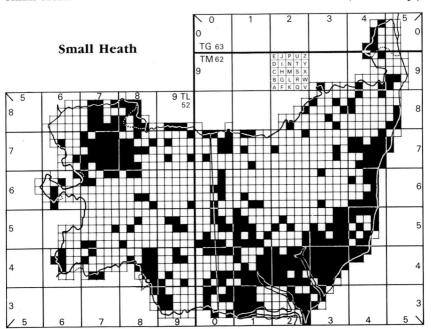

RINGLET *Aphantopus hyperantus* L.

When at rest with wings closed, the golden ringed eye-spots of the under-side (which give the Ringlet its name) readily separate the species from the somewhat similar Meadow Brown. The two species often fly together. A freshly emerged Ringlet is dark, sooty brown and appears almost black, with sharply contrasting white wing fringes when in flight. The eye spots on the upper surface are hardly visible in the majority of specimens from Suffolk.

The Ringlet is common and widespread throughout much of Britain as far north as central Scotland, but inexplicably scarce in some counties. In Suffolk it was considered *"Very common"* in the middle of the 19th century (Greene, 1857) and remained *"Common"* Bloomfield (1890). According to Morley (1937a), after that time numbers *"appreciably decreased. . . with a tendency to localisation in shady woods"*. Today the Ringlet is generally local but widespread, common in some areas, but surprisingly scarce in the south along the valley of the River Stour.

Ringlets prefer grassland in damp sheltered situations, and areas of tall grass along woodland rides and edges, hedgerows and tree-lined lanes are ideal. Although seldom found on open heathland, they may be abundant along tracks in conifer plantations in such areas. The eggs are scattered amongst the vegetation, and the larvae feed on many different grasses. The single generation of butterflies is on the wing from early July to the middle of August, but individuals soon become worn.

MILKWEED *Danaus plexippus* L.

Also known as the Monarch, this large orange-brown butterfly with dark wing veins and white spots is an American species, remarkable for its long distance migrations. It was first recorded from Britain in 1876. Though still a very scarce migrant, Milkweeds have been seen more often and in greater numbers in recent years, especially in the south-west of the country, and it seems likely that some of the butterflies may have come from the Canary Islands or Madeira where the species is now established. It is, however, unlikely that the Milkweed will ever establish itself in Britain, because the larval foodplants, the Milkweeds, *Asclepias* spp. are not indigenous.

In September 1906 a Milkweed was recorded for the first time in Suffolk and according to T.S. Barratt it was *"seen by my son whilst riding through the Avenue here in Felixstowe"* (Waller, 1929). A second, though not positively identified, was seen *"hovering about the flowers in my Framlingham garden"* (Vinter, 1933), and a third *"flying over our lawn at Rushmere Hall near Ipswich"* (King, 1937). The next was recorded in 1946 near *"Arbour Lane in Pakefield"* (Goddard, 1946), but since that date there has been only a rumour of one in the "Monarch year" of 1981. It is difficult to estimate the proportion of "British" Milkweed records which result from releases, or indeed how many have crossed the Atlantic in the holds of ships, but some do arrive here without assistance.

Ringlet

(A. Beaumont)

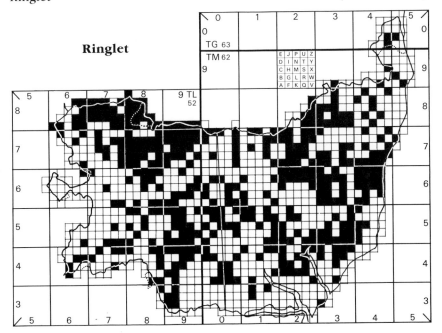

Ringlet

USEFUL ADDRESSES

Natural History and Entomology Societies

SUFFOLK NATURALISTS' SOCIETY — c/o The Museum, High Street, Ipswich IP1 3QH.

AMATEUR ENTOMOLOGISTS' SOCIETY — The Registrar, c/o 355, Hounslow Road, Hanworth, Feltham, Middlesex.

BRITISH ENTOMOLOGICAL AND NATURAL HISTORY SOCIETY — The Alpine Club, 74 South Audley Street, London W1Y 5FF.

Conservation Organisations

BRITISH BUTTERFLY CONSERVATION SOCIETY — Tudor House, Quorn, Loughborough, Leicestershire LE12 8AD.

SUFFOLK TRUST FOR NATURE CONSERVATION — Park Cottage, Saxmundham, Suffolk IP17 1DQ.

Other

SUFFOLK BIOLOGICAL RECORDS CENTRE — c/o The Museum, High Street, Ipswich IP1 3QH.

BIOLOGICAL RECORDS CENTRE — Monks Wood Experimental Station, Abbots Ripton, Huntingdon, Cambs., PE17 2LS.

USEFUL PUBLICATIONS

Identification Guides and Reference Works

BROOKS, M. and KNIGHT, C., 1982, *A complete guide to British butterflies.* Jonathan Cape, London.

GOODEN, R., 1978, *British butterflies.* David & Charles, Newton Abbot.

HEATH, J., POLLARD, E., and THOMAS, J.A., 1984, *Atlas of butterflies in Britain and Ireland.* Viking, Middlesex.

WHALLEY, P., 1984, *The Mitchell Beazley pocket guide to butterflies.* Mitchell Beazley, London.

Butterfly Gardening

CRIBB, P.W., 1982, *How to encourage butterflies to live in your garden.* Amateur Entomologists' Society, Middlesex.

OATES, M., 1985, *Garden plants for butterflies.* Brian Masterton, Fareham.

ROTHSCHILD, M., and FARRELL, C., 1983, *The butterfly gardener.* Michael Joseph, London.

REFERENCES

ANON., 1872, *Pieris Daplidice* in Suffolk. *Entomologist*, **5** : 215.

ANON., 1908, Entomologist's calendar. Note. *Country-side*, **7** : 100.

ANON., 1932, Small Blue butterfly. *Trans. Suffolk Nat. Soc.*, **2** : 84.

ANON., 1936, Proceedings. *Trans. Suffolk Nat. Soc.*, **3** : cix.

ANON., 1943. Proceedings. *Trans. Suffolk Nat. Soc.*, **5** : xlv.

ANON., 1945a, Phenomenal immigration of whites. *Trans. Suffolk Nat. Soc.*, **5** : 225.

ANON., 1945b, Proceedings, 1st October. *Trans. Suffolk Nat. Soc.*, **5** : xc-xciv.

ANON., 1947a, Swallow-tails in Suffolk. *Trans. Suffolk Nat. Soc.*, **6** : 137.

ANON., 1947b, Butterflies. *Lowestoft & North Suffolk Field Naturalists' Club*, 2nd Annual Report., **1**(2) : 47-49.

ANON., 1948, Butterflies. *Lowestoft and North Suffolk Field Naturalists' Club*, 3rd Annual Report, **1**(3) : 70-72.

ANON., 1952, Butterflies. *Lowestoft and North Suffolk Field Naturalists' Club*, 7th Annual Report, **1**(7) : 220-223.

ANON., 1958a, Camberwell Beauty. *Trans. Suffolk Nat. Soc.*, **11** : 90.

ANON., 1958b, Insects, butterflies. *Lowestoft and North Suffolk Field Naturalists' Club*, 13th Annual Report, **2**(3) : 79-80.

ANON., 1959, Newmarket Field Club. Proceedings. *Trans. Suffolk Nat. Soc.*, **11** : 280.

ANON., 1969, Insect report. *Lowestoft and North Suffolk Field Naturalists' Club*, 24th Annual Report, **3**(4) : 118-119.

ANON., 1975, Insect report. *Lowestoft and North Suffolk Field Naturalists' Club*, 30th Annual Report, **3**(10) : 431 -2.

ANON., 1976, Insect Report. *Lowestoft & North Suffolk Field Naturalists' Club*, 31st Annual Report, **4**(1) : 41.

ASTON, A.E., 1959, Collecting in 1958. *Trans. Suffolk Nat. Soc.*, **11** : 140.

ASTON, A.E., 1966, Lepidoptera at Weston, 1965. *Trans Suffolk Nat. Soc.*, **13** : 171-4.

BAKER, W.H., 1900, Rare butterflies, *East Anglian Daily Times*, August 17th, p. 5.

BARRETT, C.G., 1893, *The Lepidoptera of the British Isles*, Vol. 1. Reeve, London.

BEAUFOY, S., 1945, Bentley butterflies. *Trans. Suffolk Nat. Soc.*, **5** : 225-6.

BEAUFOY, S., 1953, The Purple Emperor in Suffolk. *Trans. Suffolk Nat. Soc.*, **8** : 131.

BEAUFOY, S., 1956, Camberwell Beauty. *Trans. Suffolk Nat. Soc.*, **10** : 78.

BEAUFOY, S., 1960, Lepidoptera rearing notes, 1959-60. *Trans. Suffolk Nat. Soc.*, **11** : 417.

BEAUFOY, S., 1970, Suffolk butterflies from 1945. *Trans. Suffolk Nat. Soc.*, **15** : 135-137.

BEAUFOY, S., 1971, Speckled Wood (*Pararge aegeria*) in Suffolk. *Trans. Suffolk Nat. Soc.*, **15** : 402.

BLACKIE, J.E.H., 1948, *Colias hyale* in Suffolk. *Entomologist*, **81** : 244.

BLACKIE, J.E.H., 1951, The range and distribution of *Agapetes galathea* L. *Entomologist*, **84** : 132-5.

BLOOMFIELD, E.N., 1890, *The Lepidoptera of Suffolk*. Wesley, London.

BRADLEY, J.D., and FLETCHER, D.S., 1979, *A recorder's log book or label list of British butterflies and moths*. Curwen, London.

BRETHERTON, R.F., 1951a, Our lost butterflies and moths. *Entomologist's Gaz.*, **2** : 211-240.

BRETHERTON, R.F., 1951b, The early history of the Swallow-tail butterfly (*Papilio machaon* L.) in England. *Entomologist's Rec. J. Var.*, **63** : 206-211.

BRETHERTON, R.F., and CHALMERS-HUNT, J.M. 1985, The immigration of Lepidoptera to the British Isles in 1981, 1982, 1983: a supplementary note. *Entomologist's Rec. J. Var.*, **97** : 76-84.

BROOKS, M., and KNIGHT, C., 1982, *A complete guide to British butterflies.* Jonathan Cape, London.

BROWN, T., 1858, *Pieris Daplidice.* Entomologist's Weekly Intelligencer, 4 : 178.

BURTON, G., 1940, Fritillary butterfly laid down. *Trans. Suffolk Nat. Soc.,* 4 : 206.

BURTON, P.J., 1941, The Dyers-weed, *Genista tinctoria,* and its insect fauna. *Trans. Suffolk Nat. Soc.,* 4 : 242.

BURTON, P.J., 1944, *Pamphila lineola,* Ochs., expands. *Trans. Suffolk Nat. Soc.,* 5 : 163.

BUTTERS, E.A., 1934, The Purple Emperor butterfly. *Trans. Suffolk Nat. Soc.,* 2 : 290.

CHALMERS-HUNT, J.M., 1977a, The 1976 invasion of the Camberwell Beauty (*Nymphalis antiopa* L.) *Entomologist's Rec. J. Var.,* 89 : 89-105.

CHALMERS-HUNT, J.M., 1977b, Post hibernation appearance of the Camberwell Beauty (*Nymphalis antiopa* L.) in 1977, and some additional records for 1976. *Entomologist's Rec. J. Var.,* 89 : 248-9.

CHATTERS, C., 1985, The heaths of South-west Suffolk. *Trans. Suffolk Nat. Soc.,* 21 : 65-72.

CHIPPERFIELD, H.E., 1956, Suffolk notes for 1956. *Trans. Suffolk Nat. Soc.,* 10 : 46.

CHIPPERFIELD, H.E., 1969, Suffolk Lepidoptera in 1968. *Trans. Suffolk Nat. Soc.,* 14 : 214-16.

CHIPPERFIELD, H.E., 1977, Suffolk Lepidoptera, 1976. *Trans. Suffolk Nat. Soc.,* 17 : 225-227.

CHIPPERFIELD, H.E., 1978, Suffolk Lepidoptera in 1977. *Trans. Suffolk Nat. Soc.,* 17 : 381-87.

CHIPPERFIELD, H.E., 1983, Suffolk Lepidoptera in 1982. *Trans. Suffolk Nat. Soc.,* 19 : 333-6.

COPINGER HILL, B., 1941, Another *Vanessa Antiopa,* Linn. *Trans. Suffolk Nat. Soc.,* 4 : 263.

CRANBROOK, J. D., 1958, Myxomatosis in Suffolk. *Trans. Suffolk Nat. Soc.,* 11 : 91.

COTTAM, A., 1900, *Argynnis Niobe,* var. *Eris* taken in England. *Entomologist's Rec. J. Var.,* 36 : 41-42.

CURTIS, J., 1831, *British entomology,* London.

DALE, C.W., 1887, Historical notes on *Aporia crataegi* in England. *Entomologist's mon. Mag.,* 24 : 38-39.

DALE, C.W., 1890, *The history of our British butterflies.* Kempster, London.

DALE, C.W., 1902, Historical notes on *Lycaena acis* in Britain. *Entomologist's Rec. J. Var.,* 38 : 76-79.

DAVEY, G., 1943, At Walsham-le-Willows. *Trans. Suffolk Nat. Soc.,* 5 : 111.

DELTA, 1837, Art. XXX. — Notes of captures. *Entomological Magazine.,* 4 : 230-34.

DENNIS, R.L.H., 1977, *The British butterfies. Their origin and establishment.* Classey, Oxford.

DENNIS, R.L.H., 1984, Egg-laying sites of the Common Blue butterfly *Polyommatus icarus* (Rottemberg) (Lepidoptera: Lycaenidae): the edge effect and beyond the edge. *Entomologist's Gaz.,* 35 : 85-93.

DUFFEY, E., 1976, *Breckland* in *Nature in Norfolk a Heritage in Trust.* Jarrold, Norwich.

EAREY, D.A., 1977, Migrating Red Admirals. *News Br. Butterfly Conserv. Soc.,* 18 : 4.

ELLIS, E. A., 1984, Butterflies of Norfolk in the 19th and 20th centuries. *Trans. Norfolk Norwich Nat. Soc.,* 26 : 321-334.

FINDLAY, R., YOUNG, M.R. and FINDLAY, J.A., 1983, Orientation behaviour in the Grayling butterfly: thermoregulation or crypsis? *Ecol. Entomol.,* 8 : 145-53.

FORD, E.B., 1977, *Butterflies.* 4th Ed., Collins, London.

FRENCH, G.M., 1936, Observations. Comma reaches the North Sea. *Trans. Suffolk Nat. Soc.,* 3 : 190.

FROHAWK, F.W., 1934a, *The complete book of British butterflies.* Ward Lock, London.

FROHAWK, F. W., 1934b, The Purple Emperor butterfly. *Trans. Suffolk Nat. Soc.,* **2** : 290.

FROHAWK, F.W., 1941, Our butterflies of yore. *Trans. Suffolk Nat. Soc.,* **4** : 258-9.

GARNESS, W., 1857, Lepidoptera near Bungay, Suffolk. *Naturalist,* **7** : 273.

GARNETT, D.G., 1952, *Vanessa cardui,* Linn. at Thorpeness. *Trans. Suffolk Nat. Soc.,* **8** : 41.

GEORGE, W.S., 1965, And suddenly they're here. *Trans. Suffolk Nat. Soc.,* **13** : 27-28.

GEORGE, W.S. 1969, The fighting caterpillars of the Orange-tip butterfly. *Trans. Suffolk Nat. Soc.,* **14** : 212-3.

GILLES, W.S., 1932, Lepidoptera in 1930. *Trans. Suffolk Nat. Soc.,* **2** : 83.

GILLES, W.S., 1934, The Purple Emperor butterfly. *Trans. Suffolk Nat. Soc.,* **2** : 289.

GODDARD, J., 1943, Larva of *Machaon* in Suffolk. *Trans. Suffolk Nat. Soc.,* **5** :110.

GODDARD, J., 1946, The fourth Milkweed butterfly in Suffolk. *Trans. Suffolk Nat. Soc.,* **6** : 64-65.

GOLDSMITH, E.T., 1952-3, The Holly Blue, *Celastrina (Cyaniris) Argiolus. Trans. Suffolk Nat. Soc.,* **8** : 81-2.

GREENE, J., 1857, List of Lepidoptera occurring in the county of Suffolk. *Naturalist,* **7** : 253-8.

HARWOOD, W.H., 1906. *Eugonia (Vanessa) polychloros. Entomologist,* **39** : 118.

HASLAM, I., 1955, Myxomatosis in East Suffolk. *Trans. Suffolk Nat. Soc.,* **9** : 213-15.

HEATH, J., POLLARD, E. and THOMAS, J.A., 1984, *Atlas of butterflies in Britain and Ireland.* Viking, England.

HELE, N.F., 1870, *Notes or jottings about Aldeburgh, Suffolk.* Russell Smith, London.

HIGGINS, L.G. and RILEY, N.D., 1983, *A field guide to the butterflies of Britain and Europe.* Collins, London.

HIND, W.M., 1889, *The flora of Suffolk.* Gurney and Jackson, London.

HOWARTH, T.G., 1973, *South's British butterflies.* Warne, London.

HUNT, A.L., 1872, *Argynnis Lathonia* and *Pieris Daplidice* at Aldeburgh, Suffolk. *Entomologist,* **6** : 236.

IRWIN, A.G., 1984, The Large Copper, *Lycaena dispar dispar* (Haworth) in the Norfolk Broads. *Entomologist's Rec. J. Var.,* **96** : 212-3.

JERMYN, L., 1824, *The butterfly collector's vade mecum: or a synoptical table of English butterflies.* 1st. Ed., Ipswich.

JERMYN, L., 1827, *The butterfly collector's vade mecum.* 2nd Ed., Ipswich.

JERMYN, L., 1836, *The butterfly collector's vade mecum; with a synoptical table of British butterflies.* 3rd. Ed., Longman, Whittaker and Pawsey, London.

KING, R.M., 1937, Another *Anosia plexippus,* L. *Trans. Suffolk Nat. Soc.,* **3** : 288.

KNAGGS, H.G., 1872, Notes on new and rare British Lepidoptera (excepting Tineina) in 1871. *Entomologist's Annual,* pp. 107-11.

LONG, C.F., 1872, *Argynnis Lathonia* at Ipswich. *Entomologist,* **6** : 236.

LUCKENS, C.J., 1978, *Euphydryas aurinia* Rott. in Britain: notes on distribution and life history. *Entomologist's Rec. J. Var.,* **90** : 108-112.

LUCKENS, C.J., 1980. The Heath Fritillary, *Mellicta athalia* Rott. in Britain: notes on distribution and ecology. *Entomologist's Rec. J. Var.,* **92** : 229-234.

MENDEL, H., 1984, A tour round the vice-counties of Suffolk. *Trans. Suffolk Nat. Soc.,* **20** : 1-9.

MILLER, S.H., and SKERTCHLY, S.B.J., 1878, *The fenland: past and present.* Leach, Wisbech.

MOORE, J.L., 1944, The annual Camberwell Beauty. *Trans. Suffolk Nat. Soc.,* **5** : 163.

MORLEY, A.M., and CHALMERS-HUNT, J.M., 1959, Some observations on the Crimson Ringed butterfly (*Parnassius apollo* L.) in Britain. *Entomologist's Rec. J. Var.,* **71** : 273-6.

MORLEY, C., 1920, Suffolk Butterflies. *East Anglian Daily Times*, 14th August.

MORLEY, C., 1932a, Wood-white butterfly in Suffolk. *Trans. Suffolk Nat. Soc.*, 2 : 84.

MORLEY, C., 1932b, Speckled-wood butterfly's extinction. *Trans. Suffolk Nat. Soc.*, 2 : 85-86.

MORLEY, C.(Ed), 1933a, Swallow-tails in Suffolk. *Trans. Suffolk Nat. Soc.*, 2 : 182.

MORLEY, C., 1933b, Spread of White Admirals. *Trans. Suffolk Nat. Soc.*, 2 : 182-3.

MORLEY, C., 1934, No *Vanessa Antiopa*, L. *Trans. Suffolk Nat. Soc.*, 2 : 290.

MORLEY, C., (Ed.), 1937a, *The Lepidoptera of Suffolk*. Suffolk Naturalists' Society.

MORLEY, C., (Ed), 1937b, Influx of Comma butterflies. *Trans. Suffolk Nat. Soc.*, 3 : 289-90.

MORLEY, C., (Ed.), 1938, The Lepidoptera of Suffolk. *Addenda et corrigenda*. *Trans. Suffolk Nat. Soc.*, 4 : 31-35.

MORLEY, C., 1941, Our pervasion by *Vanessa c-album*, Linn. *Trans. Suffolk Nat. Soc.*, 4 : 261-2.

MORLEY, C. (Ed.), 1942, Butterflies of 1942. *Trans. Suffolk Nat. Soc.*, 5 : 43-44.

MORLEY,C., 1943, Gregarious sleep of *Pararge Megaera*. *Trans. Suffolk Nat. Soc.*, 5 : 109.

MORLEY, C., 1945a, Suffolk Swallow-tails in 1945. *Trans. Suffolk Nat. Soc.*, 5 : 180-82.

MORLEY, C., (Ed.) 1945b, The annual *Vanessa antiopa*, L. *Trans. Suffolk Nat. Soc.*, 5 : 223.

MORLEY, C., (Ed.), 1946, At least three *Vanessa antiopa*, L. *Trans. Suffolk Nat. Soc.*, 6 : 65.

MORLEY, C., (Ed.), 1947a, Eight Suffolk *Vanessa Antiopa*, Linn., in 1947. *Trans. Suffolk Nat. Soc.*, 6 : 137.

MORLEY, C., (Ed.), 1947b, A "clouded yellow year". *Trans. Suffolk Nat. Soc.*, 6 : 139-40.

MORLEY, C., (Ed.), 1947c, Genial autumn.*Trans. Suffolk Nat. Soc.*, 6 :144-5.

MORLEY, C.,(Ed.), 1948, Swallow-tails and an Emperor. *Trans. Suffolk Nat. Soc.*, 6 : 240.

MORLEY, C., (Ed.), 1949, Scarce Clouded-yellow butterflies. *Trans. Suffolk Nat. Soc.*, 7 : 30.

MORRIS, F.O., 1857, *A History of British butterflies*. Groombridge, London.

NEWMAN, E., 1870-71, *The illustrated natural history of British butterflies and moths*. Allen, London.

NURSE., J.E. 1937, Large Tortoiseshell butterflies. *Trans. Suffolk Nat. Soc.*, 3 : 289.

PAGET, C.J., and J., 1834, *Sketch of the natural history of Yarmouth and its neighbourhood containing catalogues of the species of animals, birds, reptiles, fish, insects and plants, at present known*. Longman Rees, London.

PLATTEN, E.W., 1941a, An unrecorded *Argynnis lathonia*, L. *Trans. Suffolk Nat. Soc.*, 4 : 260-261.

PLATTEN, E.W., 1941b, Our large fritillaries. *Trans. Suffolk Nat. Soc.*, 4 : 259-260.

PLATTEN, E.W., 1943, Another notable survival.*Trans. Suffolk Nat. Soc.*, 5 : 110.

PLATTEN, E.W., 1946, A Bath White in Suffolk. *Trans. Suffolk Nat. Soc.*, 6 : 64.

POLLARD, E., 1979, Population ecology and change in range of the White Admiral butterfly *Ladoga camilla* L. in England. *Ecol. Entomol.*, 4 : 61-74.

POLLARD, E. and HALL, M.L., 1980, Possible movement of *Gonepteryx rhamni* (L.) (Lepidoptera: Pieridae) between hibernating and breeding areas. *Entomologist's Gaz.* 31 : 217-220.

POSTANS, R.B., 1858, Suffolk Lepidoptera. *Naturalist*, 8 : 259-60.

RAIT-SMITH, W., 1938, The Brocklehurst collection. *Entomologist*, 71 : 92-95.

RILEY, N.D., 1947, *Colias hyale* records. *Entomologist*, 80 : 291.

ROBERTSON, T.S., 1980, Seasonal variation in *Pararge aegeria* (L.) (Lepidoptera: Satyridae): a biometrical study. *Entomologist's Gaz.*, 31 : 151-6.

ROWLAND BROWN, H., 1899, *Chrysophanus dispar*. *Entomologist's Rec. J. Var.*, 11 : 277-278.

SIMPSON, F.W., 1940, *Apatura Iris*, Linn., persists. *Trans. Suffolk Nat. Soc.*, 4 : 204.

SIMPSON, F.W., 1982, *Simpson's flora of Suffolk*. Suffolk Naturalists' Society.

SMART, H.D., 1918, *Aricia medon*, ab. *artaxerxes*, in Suffolk. Entomologist, **51** : 92.

SPENCER, H.E.P., 1933, The Purple Emperor nowadays. *Trans. Suffolk Nat. Soc.*, **2** : 103-4.

STAINTON, H. T., 1857, *A manual of British butterflies and moths*. Van Voorst, London.

STEEL, C., 1984, The White-letter Hairstreak survey. *News Br. Butterfly Conserv. Soc.*, no. 32 : 31-35.

STEPHENS, J.F., 1827-28, *Illustrations of British Entomology. Haustellata*, Vol *1*. Baldwin & Cradock, London.

STUBBS, A.E., 1985, Is there a future for butterfly collecting in Britain? *Proc. Trans. Br. ent. nat. Hist. Soc.*, **18** : 65-73.

THOMAS, J., and WEBB, N., 1984, *Butterflies of Dorset*. Dorset Natural History & Archaeological Society, Dorchester.

TICKNER, B., 1941, Observations. *Trans. Suffolk Nat. Soc.*, **4** : 260.

TILLETT, W.T., 1857, Captures near Thetford. *Entomologist's Weekly Intelligencer*, **2** : 93.

TUTT, J.W., 1905-1914, *British butterflies*. 4 vols, Elliot Stock, London.

VINTER, C.H.S., 1929, An Apollo butterfly on the Suffolk coast. *Trans. Suffolk Nat. Soc.*, **1** : 13-14.

VINTER, C.H.S., 1933, *Trans. Suffolk Nat. Soc.*, **2** : 104.

VINTER, C.H.S., 1939, Butterflies of 1939. *Trans. Suffolk Nat. Soc.*, **4** : 127-128.

VINTER, C.H.S., 1942a, *Argynnis dia*, a butterfly new to Suffolk. *Trans. Suffolk Nat. Soc.*, **5** : 1-3.

VINTER, C.H.S., 1942b, Butterflies of 1942. *Trans. Suffolk Nat. Soc.*, **5** : 43.

VINTER, C.H.S., 1943, Butterflies of 1943. *Trans. Suffolk Nat. Soc.*, **5** : 112-113.

VINTER, C.H.S., 1944, Suffolk Lepidoptera in 1944. *Trans. Suffolk Nat. Soc.*, **5** : 161-2.

VINTER, C.H.S., 1946, Suffolk Lepidoptera in 1946. *Trans. Suffolk Nat. Soc.*, **6** : 62-63.

VINTER, C.H.S., 1947, Suffolk Lepidoptera in 1947. *Trans. Suffolk Nat. Soc.*, **6** : 136.

VINTER, C.H.S., 1950, Suffolk butterflies of 1950. *Trans. Suffolk Nat. Soc.*, **7** : 88-89.

WALKER, J.J., 1904, Some notes on the Lepidoptera of the 'Curtis' collection of British insects. *Entomologist's mon. Mag.*, **40** : 187-194.

WALLER, A.P., 1929, The Lepidoptera of Suffolk. Second Supplement. *Trans. Suffolk Nat. Soc.*, **1** : 30-38.

WALLER, A.P., 1952-3, Further notes on Suffolk Lepidoptera in 1952. *Trans. Suffolk Nat. Soc.*, **8** : 37.

WALLER, T.N., 1935, On the local *Niobe* butterfly. *Trans. Suffolk Nat. Soc.*, **3** : 6-9.

WARREN, M.S., 1984, The biology and status of the Wood White butterfly, *Leptidea sinapis* (L.) (Lepidoptera: Pieridae) in the British Isles. *Entomologist's Gaz.*, **35** : 207-223.

WATERFIELD, 1944, *Machaon* larvae laid down. *Trans. Suffolk Nat. Soc.*, **5** : 162-3.

WEBSTER, J.A., 1941, Westleton Lepidoptera. *Trans. Suffolk Nat. Soc.*, **4** : 258.

WEST, B.K., 1982, *Pieris rapae* L. and *Cardaria draba* (Cruciferae) as a larval foodplant. *Entomologist's Rec. J. Var.*, **94** : 72.

WILLIAMS, C.B., 1971, *Insect migration*, Collins, London.

WORMS, C.G.M. de, 1952, Collecting Lepidoptera in the eastern counties; some reminiscences. *Trans. Suffolk Nat. Soc.*, **8** : 43-46.

WORMS, C.G.M. de, 1952-3, Notes on British Lepidoptera for 1952. *Trans. Suffolk Nat. Soc.*, **8** : 74-76.

WORMS, C.G.M. de, 1959, Two visits to Suffolk during 1959. *Trans. Suffolk Nat. Soc.*, **11** : 253.

WORMS, C.G.M. de, 1973, A review of Lepidoptera in Britain during 1972. *Trans. Suffolk Nat. Soc.*, **16** : 173-6.

WORMS, C.G.M. de, 1979, A review of some butterflies and moths in Suffolk during the past fifty years. *Trans. Suffolk Nat. Soc.*, **18** : 63-69.

126

WRATTISLAW, A.H., 1865, *Argynnis Lathonia,* etc. at Aldeburgh and Bury. *Entomologist,* 2 : 340.

WRATTISLAW, A.H., 1870, Entomology in the county of Suffolk. *Proceedings of the Suffolk Institute of Archaeology and Natural History,* 4 : 217-222.

WRATTISLAW, A.H., 1886, Captures at Bury St. Edmunds. *Entomologist,* 3 : 189.

INDEX OF SPECIES